MW00607678

Program Guide

For Effective Alcohol-Use Prevention in Schools and Communities

Developed from Research Funded by the National Institute on Alcohol Abuse and Alcoholism

Cheryl L. Perry, Ph.D., Carolyn L. Williams, Ph.D.,
and Sara Veblen-Mortenson, M.S.W., M.P.H.

HAZELDEN®

Hazelden
Center City, Minnesota 55012
hazelden.org

© 2009 by Hazelden Foundation
All rights reserved. Published 2009
Printed in the United States of America

Some material contained in *Program Guide* has been adapted from *Supercharged! Strategies That Worked in Project Northland Communities* (Hazelden, 2000).

Unless a statement on the page grants permission to duplicate or permission has been obtained from the publisher, no part of this publication may be reproduced, stored in a retrieval system, or transmitted in any form or by any means—electronic, mechanical, photocopying, recording, scanning, or otherwise. Failure to comply with these terms may expose you to legal action and damages for copyright infringement.

ISBN: 978-1-59285-727-2

Editor's note

Alcoholics Anonymous and AA are registered trademarks of Alcoholics Anonymous World Services, Inc.

Cover design by Kinne Design
Interior design and typesetting by Kinne Design
Illustrations © by Michael Thone
Illustrations from *Slick Tracy* by Glenn Quist

Hazelden, a national nonprofit organization founded in 1949, helps people reclaim their lives from the disease of addiction. Built on decades of knowledge and experience, Hazelden offers a comprehensive approach to addiction that addresses the full range of patient, family, and professional needs, including treatment and continuing care for youth and adults, research, higher learning, public education and advocacy, and publishing.

A life of recovery is lived "one day at a time." Hazelden publications, both educational and inspirational, support and strengthen lifelong recovery. In 1954, Hazelden published *Twenty-Four Hours a Day,* the first daily meditation book for recovering alcoholics, and Hazelden continues to publish works to inspire and guide individuals in treatment and recovery, and their loved ones. Professionals who work to prevent and treat addiction also turn to Hazelden for evidence-based curricula, informational materials, and videos for use in schools, treatment programs, and correctional programs.

Through published works, Hazelden extends the reach of hope, encouragement, help, and support to individuals, families, and communities affected by addiction and related issues.

For questions about Hazelden publications, please call **800-328-9000** or visit us online at **hazelden.org/bookstore**.

What Is the Purpose of This Guide?

The purpose of the *Program Guide* is to provide step-by-step instructions on how to implement the Project Northland underage alcohol-use prevention series. It is important that you read through this guide before beginning implementation.

Throughout the guide, you will see the following:

RESEARCH FACTS

These facts highlight some of the important research findings of Project Northland's distinguished author-researcher team and other researchers.

PROFESSIONAL HIGHLIGHTS

These features are a sampling of experiences shared by many professionals who have worked with Project Northland in a variety of settings over the years.

PROGRAM TIPS

These tips and strategies, gleaned from others' experiences, will make program implementation easier for you.

PREVENTION RAINBOW

This icon corresponds to the prevention framework described on page 3. It helps increase your awareness of which domains (adolescent, family, peers, school, community, or society) are impacted by different parts of Project Northland.

Also, you will find thumbnails of relevant materials from the CD-ROM.

How to Use the CD-ROM

This *Program Guide* comes with a CD-ROM that contains resources such as worksheets, templates, and resource lists to support the Project Northland program. All of these resources are either in PDF format (which can be accessed using Adobe Reader) or in Microsoft Word. If you do not have Adobe Reader, you can download it free of charge at http://www.adobe.com.

Duplicating this page is illegal. Do not copy this material without written permission from the publisher.

Whenever you see this icon ⬚, it signals that a copy of the resource being discussed is on the CD-ROM. There will be a number on the icon that corresponds to the number of the document on the CD-ROM.

To access the resources on the CD-ROM, put the disc in your computer's CD-ROM player. Open your version of Adobe Reader or Microsoft Word, and then open the documents by clicking on the ones you wish to use. The PDF documents cannot be modified, but they can be printed to support your implementation without concern of copyright infringement. For a complete list of the resources included on your *Program Guide* CD-ROM, please see pages 157–161 of this manual. This list is also on your CD-ROM. ⬚

How to Use the DVD

This *Program Guide* comes with a DVD that provides an overview of Project Northland. You may use this video in staff and parent trainings, and for program promotion with sponsors and school-related groups such as your school board, parent organization, or community coalition.

When you see this icon 💻, you should use the accompanying DVD.

The *Program Guide* DVD includes two videos to help you understand Project Northland and explain its key features to other people. The "Project Northland Overview" and "Project Northland in Action" videos each run slightly longer than sixteen minutes. The "Project Northland Overview" provides a foundation for anyone new to the program. You may wish to share it with community groups, parent groups, potential sponsors, your school board, or others. It may be shown at a staff meeting when Project Northland is first introduced. This overview is also a good introduction for administrators and groups who are considering adopting the program. "Project Northland in Action" is intended for staff members who will help deliver the program to students. It provides more detail about the key features of each curriculum.

* * *

Duplicating this page is illegal. Do not copy this material without written permission from the publisher.

What Do People Say About Project Northland?

"I absolutely love Project Northland, and so do the students!"

— SHALA GODWIN, CERTIFIED PREVENTION PROFESSIONAL
Teacher and Program Coordinator

"Project Northland is powerfully engaging for students and certainly youth-centered. The visual elements are very appealing to youth and adults. The program gets youth thinking about their futures."

— INEZ R. DRUMMOND, ED.D.
Manager, Safe and Drug-Free Schools and Communities,
Chicago Public Schools

"One of [my] favorite initiatives, both because of its curb appeal and because of promising data, is Project Northland. Project Northland is an alcohol prevention program that addresses alcohol use at multiple levels . . . The program approaches the topic of alcohol use among adolescents from a very comprehensive perspective . . . The context and strategies used in Project Northland are grade specific . . . Data indicate that the program works."

— AARON WHITE, PH.D.
*Keeping Adolescence Healthy: Exploring the Issues Facing Today's
Kids and Communities*

Duplicating this page is illegal. Do not copy this material without written permission from the publisher.

v

CONTENTS

Duplicating this page is illegal. Do not copy this material without written permission from the publisher.

Duplicating this page is illegal. Do not copy this material without written permission from the publisher.

◦   •   ◦

Duplicating this page is illegal. Do not copy this material without written permission from the publisher.

We are grateful for and acknowledge the support, cooperation, and partnership of students, parents, teachers, community members, and administrators in our participating Minnesota and Chicago public schools.

The Minnesota school districts included Aitkin, Babbitt-Embarrass, Biwabik, Carlton, Coleraine, Cook County, Deer River, Ely, Esko, Floodwood, Grand Rapids, Hermantown, Hibbing, Hill City, McGregor, Mountain Iron-Buhl, Nashwauk-Keewatin, Nett Lake, Proctor, St. Louis County, South Koochiching, Toivola-Meadowlands, Tower-Soudan, Virginia, and Wrenshall. In Chicago, Dr. Inez Drummond, manager of the Office of Specialized Services, Chicago Public Schools, served as our primary district-level contact and helped us navigate the logistics of the school district in a timely and positive manner. Special acknowledgments go to our Minnesota- and Chicago-based community organizers for implementation of the school/youth and/or community interventions. In Minnesota, that included Tom Burman, Lynette Eck, Kathy Lingren, Judy Lundquist, Judie Maki, Russell Maki, James Pavlek, Peter Pierson, and Sue Wetschka. In Chicago, the organizers included Mirlene Cadichon, Britt Garton, Francisco Hernandez, Tamika Hinton, Carol G. Johnson, Oscar Lester, Angelique Orr, Maria T. Ramos, Gloria R. Riley, and Kate Weinans, and the community action team members who worked diligently on alcohol-use prevention initiatives. Special thanks go to our Youth Action Team coordinators (Minnesota High School phase).

Other management, development, and evaluation staff that deserve special acknowledgment and who worked on both the Minnesota and Chicago studies include Kian Farbakhsh for data analysis, Glenn Quist for graphic artistry for project materials, and Verla Johansson and Bonnie Manning for outstanding secretarial and creative support with desktop publishing and graphic design.

The studies were also fortunate to have expertise provided by Drs. Alex Wagenaar, Traci Toomey, and Rhonda Jones-Webb on the development of the community intervention, alcohol policies and ordinances, cultural adaptations, and program evaluation; the program design and implementation skills of Randi Bernstein Lachter with the youth action teams, Lara Pratt with the community and media programs, and Dr. Robert Cudeck for his advice on growth curve analysis.

Additional thanks in the Chicago study go to Karen Alfano, the evaluation director; Linda Bosma, the community organizing director during the first three

Duplicating this page is illegal. Do not copy this material without written permission from the publisher.

xi

years of the project, followed by Mirlene Cadichon during the last year of the intervention; Barb Dahlquist, Susan Fitze, Jessica Hayssen, Karen Severson, and Mary Ann Thoma-Cox, our exceptional intervention and evaluation implementation support staff; and Mary Hearst, Kari Kugler, and Keryn Pasch, our productive and bright research assistants, who helped with intervention and evaluation development and implementation.

This edition of Project Northland has benefited from the research and writing of Claire Buchwald and the thoughtful input of reviewers Debra Mayconich Baron, Becky Hudlow, and Janet Jones. Many thanks to these individuals for their important work.

The Minnesota and Chicago Project Northland studies were funded by grants from the National Institute on Alcohol Abuse and Alcoholism awarded to Dr. Cheryl L. Perry, PI (Minnesota: RO1-AA08596, 1990–1995, 1994–1995, 1995–1999), Dr. Carolyn Williams, PI (Minnesota: RO1-AA10719, 1995–1999), and Dr. Kelli A. Komro, PI (Chicago: R01-AA13458, 2001–2007; R01-AA016549, 2008–2012).

•   •   •

Duplicating this page is illegal. Do not copy this material without written permission from the publisher.

CHAPTER 1

Welcome to Project Northland!

In this chapter, you will gain a basic understanding of Project Northland and its value to you, your students, and your community.

▶▶ *What You Will Learn in Chapter 1:*

- What is Project Northland?
- What makes Project Northland effective?
- What does research show about Project Northland's effectiveness?
- How to meet national academic standards with Project Northland

What Is Project Northland?

Project Northland is a nationally recognized alcohol-use prevention program. The four Project Northland curricula include *Slick Tracy, Amazing Alternatives, Power Lines,* and *Class Action.* They are supported by this *Program Guide* for administrators and program coordinators. Project Northland was developed at the University of Minnesota from research funded by the National Institute on Alcohol Abuse and Alcoholism. This state-of-the-art alcohol-use prevention program is backed by more than eighteen years of research and more than forty-five scientific publications. A list of research articles can be found on the accompanying CD-ROM. Research has shown that, in addition to effectively achieving its alcohol prevention goals,[1] Project Northland can significantly reduce teens' marijuana and tobacco use.[2]

Project Northland interventions target all students, putting them in the category of *universal prevention efforts* (also known as primary prevention). The needs of most students for information and skills are met at this level. Universal prevention efforts differ from *selective prevention efforts,* or the specialized programs designed for students who have been identified as at risk—for example, students with a history of behavior problems or those with a family history of

Duplicating this page is illegal. Do not copy this material without written permission from the publisher.

alcoholism—and *indicated prevention efforts,* or special programs for students with identified substance abuse problems (see figure 1).

FIGURE 1

Public Health Approach to Preventing Underage Alcohol Use

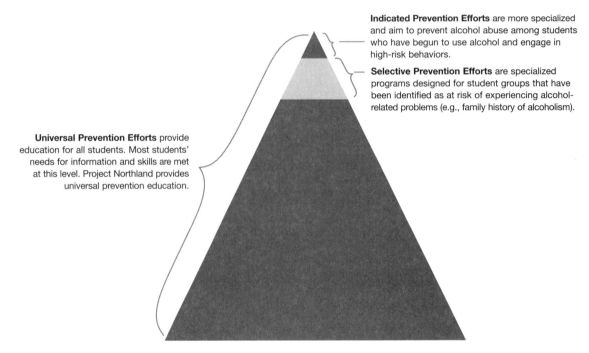

Indicated Prevention Efforts are more specialized and aim to prevent alcohol abuse among students who have begun to use alcohol and engage in high-risk behaviors.

Selective Prevention Efforts are specialized programs designed for student groups that have been identified as at risk of experiencing alcohol-related problems (e.g., family history of alcoholism).

Universal Prevention Efforts provide education for all students. Most students' needs for information and skills are met at this level. Project Northland provides universal prevention education.

Project Northland's universal alcohol-use prevention curricula are designed for young adolescents, both male and female.

What Are Project Northland's Goals?

The goals of Project Northland are to

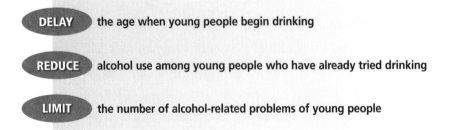

DELAY the age when young people begin drinking

REDUCE alcohol use among young people who have already tried drinking

LIMIT the number of alcohol-related problems of young people

Duplicating this page is illegal. Do not copy this material without written permission from the publisher.

What Makes Project Northland an Outstanding Prevention Program?

The Project Northland curricula invite participation and experiential learning at home, in the classroom, and in the local community. A vital aspect of Project Northland is this multifaceted approach. Prevention research shows that addressing alcohol use at multiple levels strengthens outcomes. Incorporating best practices for effective prevention, the curriculum engages students as individuals and addresses influences in the family, with peers, at school, and in the local community and broader society. Project Northland addresses these domains more comprehensively than any other prevention program.

Project Northland's conceptual framework is captured nicely in figure 2. Each Project Northland curriculum targets the various influences in the adolescents' world with developmentally appropriate interventions.

FIGURE 2

The World of the Adolescent

 **PROFESSIONAL HIGHLIGHT**

"Communities should adopt prevention interventions that include school, family, and community components." [3]

Fittingly, figure 2 places the adolescent at the center of his or her world. Each young person brings individual characteristics, like personal values, attitudes, beliefs, knowledge, behavioral skills, and personality characteristics that can contribute to his or her decision to use alcohol and other drugs—and many are addressed in Project Northland.

Although adolescence is a time of separating from the family, Project Northland interventions recognize the importance of the

Duplicating this page is illegal. Do not copy this material without written permission from the publisher.

family, as well as the diversity of today's families. Universal prevention programs like Project Northland are not intended merely for students from traditional two-parent households. Today's families often include adults other than parents who live with the student—stepparents, grandparents, foster parents, and guardians, to name a few—as well as others like siblings, cousins, or anybody with long-standing and binding ties.

As adolescents begin to separate from their families, the peer group becomes an increasingly important influence on a young person's behavior. Some of these peer groups are in the school, and others are neighborhood based or centered on sports or other extracurricular activities, including after-school jobs. Peer influences are covered extensively in each of the four Project Northland curricula.

Teachers, coaches, administrators, nurses, and others at school are role models who spend considerable time with adolescents. School policies—when enforced consistently—can be effective prevention strategies for underage drinking. After-hours school-based events can provide safe and fun alternatives to risky, unsupervised activities that can include alcohol and other drugs. Every year of Project Northland interventions includes extensive school-based programs designed to reduce underage drinking by your students.

Teens live in communities with local governments, law enforcement, merchants, media, faith-based organizations, youth-serving organizations, sports teams, and the like, all of which can have a strong positive—or negative—influence on underage drinking or other drug use. Although influences from the broader society are more distant, they can be powerful and include, as examples, state and federal laws and policies, mass media, the beverage industry, and professional sports teams. You will find Project Northland interventions target many of these influences as well.

Project Northland utilizes peer-led, experiential, activity-driven learning strategies to actively educate students. Parents

PROFESSIONAL HIGHLIGHT

"Everyone really likes it; what to do is prescribed, and the number of lessons is good."

CHEMICAL HEALTH DIVISION PLANNER, STATE DEPARTMENT OF HUMAN SERVICES (MINNESOTA)

Duplicating this page is illegal. Do not copy this material without written permission from the publisher.

and guardians are enlisted to support a "no use" message, while communities mobilize to reduce youth access to alcohol and to promote alcohol-free norms for youth. The curricula are user friendly for teachers, fun for students, inviting to parents and guardians, and effective in preventing alcohol use.

Who Is the Intended Audience?

The Project Northland interventions provide a sustained and comprehensive program for alcohol-use prevention during middle school and high school. Each program builds on materials presented and learned during earlier years. For example, Peer Leaders are introduced in *Slick Tracy* and given more training and responsibilities in *Amazing Alternatives*. Time Capsules are completed by students at the end of each curriculum and are returned to them at the beginning of the next. For best results, Project Northland implementers have their students begin with *Slick Tracy* in fifth or sixth grade, continue with *Amazing Alternatives* and *Power Lines* in grades seven and eight, and follow up with *Class Action* in high school.

There are many innovative ways to deliver Project Northland and still maintain fidelity. The curricula can fit well into advisory, homeroom, health education, social studies, science, or general life skills classes. Connections to national academic standards are referenced on pages 17–20. Project Northland has been delivered effectively by school resource officers, prevention coordinators, community coalition volunteers, and older students from high schools and colleges. Since Peer Leaders facilitate most classroom activities, adults participate more as "coaches" or "facilitators" than as educators.

Some communities may be interested in implementing Project Northland in a school-based after-school setting. Since, at present, there is no evidence indicating the effectiveness of such a model, it is important for any communities attempting this to conduct a particularly thorough program evaluation. It is also important to plan how the program will involve the majority of the student body, at the targeted grade levels, over Project Northland's entire

PROFESSIONAL HIGHLIGHT

"It's user friendly. Everything is spelled out. It's motivational for the students, and anybody could teach it. All the materials are provided."

ADMINISTRATOR
(ALABAMA)

Duplicating this page is illegal. Do not copy this material without written permission from the publisher.

three- to four-year cycle. The fidelity tools on your CD-ROM can help guide this work.

What Does Research Show about Project Northland's Effectiveness?

Project Northland grew out of the most rigorous alcohol-use prevention trial ever funded by the National Institute on Alcohol Abuse and Alcoholism (NIAAA) and was developed in a region of the country that led the nation in alcohol-related traffic fatalities. More than eighteen years of research at the University of Minnesota's Division of Epidemiology & Community Health is the foundation of the Project Northland curriculum series.

Outcomes from the original study showed that, relative to students in the control group, Project Northland participants demonstrated reduced levels of alcohol, marijuana, and cigarette use, and they displayed more resilient behaviors.[4]

Students who participated in Project Northland showed 30 percent lower weekly drinking and 20 percent lower monthly drinking. They engaged in 27 percent lower cigarette use and 27 percent lower alcohol use by the end of eighth grade. These students also demonstrated markedly lower drug use by the end of eighth grade. Intervention group students who never drank alcohol at the beginning of sixth grade showed 50 percent lower marijuana use and 37 percent lower cigarette use by the end of eighth grade.[5]

The Project Northland authors also examined the impact of Project Northland on problem behavior scales from MMPI-A— the adolescent form of the Minnesota Multiphasic Personality Inventory.[6] Students whose risk of drinking was lowered by Project Northland also demonstrated less growth of family problems and less likelihood to use both alcohol and drugs than students in the control group. This suggests that Project Northland may positively impact young lives more broadly than originally had been documented and may be of interest to parents or guardians and school districts considering adoption of an evidence-based prevention program such as Project Northland.

Duplicating this page is illegal. Do not copy this material without written permission from the publisher.

The authors conducted another large and rigorous research study to examine Project Northland's effectiveness in large, urban school districts. The study, conducted in Chicago, did not confirm program efficacy in urban communities with low-income and minority youth. Chicago educators liked Project Northland, and participation levels were high. Secondary outcome analyses to assess the effects of each program component indicated that the home-based pieces were associated with reduced alcohol, marijuana, and tobacco use.[7] Findings of this study highlight the value of, and need for, additional research with urban communities.

For additional information about the research behind Project Northland, a publications list is available on the CD-ROM.

What Are the Project Northland Curricula?

Full Project Northland implementation includes four curricula supported by community efforts to achieve program goals:

■ **Slick Tracy,** the first curriculum in the series, uses comic-book-style activity booklets to help students and parents discuss alcohol issues. Students engage in fun peer-led activities that introduce the booklets at school. They complete these booklets—ideally with their parents, or with other significant adults as needed—to earn rewards. *Slick Tracy* culminates with a Poster Fair at which students present their own alcohol-related research projects to family, friends, and community members. The entire *Slick Tracy* program requires five thirty-minute classroom sessions, time for students to work on their projects, the one-hour Poster Fair, and a three-hour training session for Peer Leaders. Although *Slick Tracy* was originally designed for sixth graders, some communities may find it a better fit with the needs of their fifth graders. In such cases, *Slick Tracy* may be implemented in the fifth grade, but be sure to wait until seventh grade to resume Project Northland with the *Amazing Alternatives* curriculum.

Duplicating this page is illegal. Do not copy this material without written permission from the publisher.

■ **Amazing Alternatives** introduces seventh graders to "virtual classmates" through a weekly audio drama featuring students their age. Eight forty-five-minute classroom sessions include peer-led experiential activities: group discussions, games, problem-solving challenges, and role plays. These activities teach students to identify and resist influences to use alcohol. Their purpose is to change the acceptability of alcohol use and to encourage alcohol-free alternatives. The primary goal is to delay the onset of youth alcohol use. Parent and guardian participation materials encourage family communication and involvement.

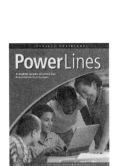

■ **Power Lines** brings into eighth-grade classrooms the community's range of professional and political powers that influence youth alcohol choices. The Anthony Parker audio drama and Franklin community meeting activity provide a dramatic context for the interplay of different groups around the youth alcohol controversy in a fictional community. Through small-group projects, students learn about the influence of real powers in their own communities. These projects empower eighth graders with the opportunity to become positive community influences within their neighborhoods, schools, and peer groups, and with younger students. *Power Lines's* eight forty-five-minute classroom sessions reinforce and build upon the messages and behaviors learned in *Slick Tracy* and *Amazing Alternatives.* Parent participation materials are included.

■ **Class Action** is Project Northland's high school component. Including it in your implementation will strengthen your community's program outcomes. *Class Action* is an eight- to ten-session curriculum that looks at the real-world social and legal consequences of teen alcohol use. Students are divided into six legal teams to prepare and present hypothetical civil cases in which someone has been harmed as a result of underage drinking. The six cases included in *Class Action* are

- Drinking and Driving on Trial: *Foley v. Welby*
- Fetal Alcohol Syndrome on Trial: *Dixon v. Nordeen*

Duplicating this page is illegal. Do not copy this material without written permission from the publisher.

- Drinking and Violence on Trial: *Benton v. Dempsey*
- Date Rape on Trial: *Allen v. Block*
- Drinking and Vandalism on Trial: *Brown v. The Bixby Festival Planning Committee*
- School Alcohol Policies on Trial: *Hunt v. Wilson*

Using a casebook, recorded affidavits, and depositions as resources, teens build legal cases and present them to a jury of their peers.

The Project Northland Curricula

	SLICK TRACY	AMAZING ALTERNATIVES	POWER LINES	CLASS ACTION
Curriculum focus	Families communicating a no-use message about alcohol use	Peers and social norms	Community influences and social norms	Legal consequences of harm done by underage alcohol use
Designed for	Sixth grade	Seventh grade	Eighth grade	Tenth or eleventh grade
Program highlights	• Comic books • Peer Leaders • Poster Fair	• Audio drama • Peer Leaders	• Franklin "community meeting" • Research projects	Student teams receive evidence and prepare to prosecute
Special event/s	Required: Poster Fair	Recommended: *Amazing Alternatives* Fun Night/s	Required: Project presentations	Required: Mock trials
Peer Leaders	Nominated and trained	Nominated and trained	Shared leadership	Shared leadership

The materials needed to implement Project Northland include this guide; the four curriculum manuals with their accompanying CD-ROMs, audio CDs, comic books, and casebooks; and the CD-ROM and DVD that accompany this guide. Instructions for using the CD-ROM are on pages iii–iv, and a complete list of the CD-ROM materials may be found on pages 157–161.

Duplicating this page is illegal. Do not copy this material without written permission from the publisher.

How Can Community Efforts Support Project Northland's Goals?

While the Project Northland curricula do explore community issues, prevention efforts in the wider community beyond school walls can dramatically reduce environmental risk factors. For example, communities may establish new laws and policies that make it more difficult for teens to obtain alcohol, or they may improve enforcement of existing laws and policies. Community-led compliance checks, media campaigns, and alcohol-free events can all help. Chapter 3 includes more ideas about community involvement, and chapter 8 extensively discusses community coalitions and the types of support communities may offer.

About Project Northland's 2009 Edition

The prevention messages and learner outcomes that made the original Project Northland so successful have remained the same. The revised curricula are more culturally sensitive and reflect more diversity than the originals. The popular art from *Slick Tracy's* urban edition is used. Both Spanish and English single-language comic books are offered with *Slick Tracy,* and the audio recordings for *Amazing Alternatives* and *Power Lines* have been updated. Resources have been added, including this *Program Guide,* updated fidelity guidelines, sample evaluation tools, planning forms, tips, and ideas. Each component of Project Northland now includes a CD-ROM that contains many of these resources.

Why Is Alcohol the Drug Targeted by Project Northland?

Alcohol prevention is the focus of Project Northland because alcohol is the drug of choice for American teenagers. Use often begins during early adolescence. Alcohol inflicts the most harm at this age, and early use leads to serious consequences in adulthood.

Alcohol is the most commonly used drug among American youth[8] and for many, initiation of use occurs prior to age thirteen.[9]

Duplicating this page is illegal. Do not copy this material without written permission from the publisher.

Results from the 2007 nationwide Youth Risk Behavior Survey suggest that nearly one-quarter of youth begin drinking alcohol before age thirteen.[10] By eighth grade, 39 percent of youth report having used alcohol in their lifetime, and 16 percent used in the past month.[11] Of even greater concern is that nearly one in five eighth graders report ever having been drunk, and 10 percent report heavy episodic use—having had five or more drinks in a row in the previous two weeks.[12]

Such early onset of use has been associated with a number of health and social problems, including alcohol abuse and dependence, alcohol-related violence and injuries, drinking and driving, truancy, traffic crashes, risky sexual behavior, and other drug use throughout adolescence and into adulthood.[13] Some argue that early exposure to alcohol and other drugs is not the cause of later problems, but rather a result of a childhood history of conduct disorders.[14] However, a study spanning thirty years demonstrated that about half of adolescents who began drinking alcohol and using drugs before age fifteen had no history of earlier conduct problems. Furthermore, these normal young teens who began drinking and using other drugs earlier than their peers were more likely to develop substance abuse disorders as adults, test positive for herpes infections, have an early pregnancy, and be convicted of a felony than those who did not begin drinking or using drugs before age fifteen.[16]

Recent research on brain growth and development presents other compelling reasons to reduce the number of teens who drink alcohol. Contrary to past beliefs, tremendous development and maturation occurs in the brain during the second decade of life. These changes are believed to be related to important higher-order functions involving cognitive control over behavior, including decision making, mood regulation, and impulse control. For example, we now know that development of the prefrontal cortex—the region of the brain associated with critical thinking and decision making—is not completed until early adulthood.[17] The limbic system, which includes the septal area, hippocampus, and amygdala, increases in volume during adolescence.[18] The hippocampus,

RESEARCH FACT

Project Northland students who had never tried alcohol at the beginning of sixth grade showed 50 percent lower marijuana use and 37 percent lower cigarette use by the end of eighth grade.[15]

Duplicating this page is illegal. Do not copy this material without written permission from the publisher.

because of its association with learning and memory, is the subject of much current research. In addition, the brain becomes better able to work in an integrated manner as the adolescent matures because of changes that come about from synaptic pruning and myelination.[19]

As research accumulates on the development and maturation of the brain during adolescence, increasing concern is raised about the potential for harm with the introduction of a potent neurotoxin like alcohol into the adolescent's changing body. There is no information available to recommend a "safe" level of alcohol intake for adolescents. Furthermore, adolescents are cognitively immature in neurological processes related to decision making and response inhibition that can provide internal controls on alcohol intake. For these reasons, experts recommend comprehensive prevention programs like Project Northland that include interventions offering opportunities for the individual to learn and rehearse behavioral skills, as well as programs that allow the family, school, and community to provide environments conducive to no-use norms.[20] Such programs best match the immature neurological development of adolescents.

PROFESSIONAL HIGHLIGHT

Have Project Northland Customers Experienced Positive Outcomes?

"According to our survey data, collected over a period of more than fifteen years, local eighth graders exposed to Project Northland scored markedly better than their peers nationally on four key indicators: engage in binge drinking, perceive alcohol use as harmful, disapprove of alcohol use, and monthly alcohol use. Additionally, the more three-year Project Northland cycles schools had completed, the better their students scored. By contrast, local eighth graders who did not participate were 11 percent to 46 percent more likely than their national counterparts to engage in binge drinking, and they were about 12 percent more likely to have engaged in underage drinking during the past month. A survey by the University of Illinois's Center for Prevention and Research Development concurs with our local findings."

COMMUNITY COALITION DIRECTOR, REGIONAL OFFICE OF EDUCATION (ILLINOIS)

Duplicating this page is illegal. Do not copy this material without written permission from the publisher.

Introduction to Underage Alcohol Issues, on the CD-ROM, provides more information about research on both underage drinking and the adolescent brain.

Can I Expect Strong Results in My Community?

For your community to experience the greatest benefits, it is important to implement Project Northland with fidelity, that is, as closely as possible to the authors' implementation during their research. Of course, you will make some choices to meet the unique needs of your students, but there are key features of the model that need to be followed. Consulting the classroom checklists on your CD-ROM will help ensure that you include all the essentials.

There are four checklists for classroom implementation and one for communities. First, there is a general classroom checklist. This may be used by someone observing any middle-school session without advance knowledge of which session will be taught. There is also a detailed checklist for each of the three middle-school curricula. These checklists specify the main parts of each classroom session and whether each part is intended to be teacher led or peer led. The Fidelity Checklist for Project Northland Communities includes self-assessment questions for community groups supporting program implementation and evaluation.

Is Project Northland Recognized Nationally?

- The Project Northland series is included in the National Registry of Evidence-based Programs and Practices of the U.S. Department of Health and Human Services' Substance Abuse and Mental Health Services Administration (SAMHSA).

- Project Northland is listed as an Exemplary Program by the Office of Juvenile Justice and Delinquency Prevention (U.S. Department of Justice) and the Office of Safe and Drug-Free Schools (U.S. Department of Education).

Duplicating this page is illegal. Do not copy this material without written permission from the publisher.

- *Making the Grade* by Drug Strategies—a nonprofit research institute that supports efforts to decrease the demand for drugs through prevention, education, treatment, law enforcement, and community initiatives—has bestowed its "A" rating upon the program.

- Project Northland meets the Principles of Effectiveness outlined by the National Institute on Drug Abuse (NIDA) for Safe and Drug-Free Schools.

Summary

In order to make the most of Project Northland in your community, plan your implementation with long-term sustainability built into every facet. Although "Sustaining Your Program" is the final chapter in this guide, you may find it worthwhile to jump ahead to page 147 and skim it before reading the remaining chapters in sequence. In order to maintain and build upon your successes for many years ahead, you will want to implement Project Northland with fidelity, create a sustainable program, and evaluate your program well for continuous improvement.

Duplicating this page is illegal. Do not copy this material without written permission from the publisher.

Project Northland Scope and Sequence

TOPIC	SLICK TRACY (6th Grade)	AMAZING ALTERNATIVES (7th Grade)
Students will demonstrate the ability to:		
Facts about Alcohol	• describe myths about alcohol use • know basic facts about alcohol (e.g., alcohol is a depressant) • know the short- and long-term consequences of alcohol use	• review important facts related to underage alcohol use • review negative consequences of underage alcohol use
Reasons for Alcohol Use	• identify false reasons why people drink alcohol (e.g., it makes them "cool"; they have more fun)	• identify reasons why some people their age use alcohol
Consequences of Alcohol Use	• know that alcohol affects the ability to think clearly and make good decisions • know that people can die from drinking too much alcohol • describe other negative consequences of alcohol use	• define the word "consequence" • explain negative consequences of alcohol use • understand that one person's alcohol use affects other people • understand that alcohol use can get in the way of personal goals • identify negative consequences that show why a seventh grader should not use alcohol
Peer Pressure and Alcohol Use	• identify different kinds of peer pressure • identify ways they are pressured to use alcohol • identify ways to resist peer pressure to use alcohol • practice resisting peer pressure to use alcohol	• describe how peer pressure to use alcohol has changed since sixth grade • explain ways seventh graders are influenced to use alcohol • identify positive, assertive ways to resist offers of alcohol • practice saying "no" to alcohol • discuss, compare, and assess ways to effectively resist pressures to use alcohol
Evaluating Alcohol Advertisements	• identify the false messages in alcohol advertising • identify the false alcohol messages on TV and in movies • describe how alcohol advertising influences a person's thinking • evaluate alcohol advertising messages	• define the word "media" • review methods the alcohol industry uses to attract drinkers • identify false messages in alcohol advertising • interpret different types of alcohol advertisements and promotions
Finding Positive Alternatives to Alcohol	• identify many beverages that do not contain alcohol • describe ways to have fun without alcohol	• define the word "alternative" • identify positive alternatives to using alcohol • practice finding positive alternatives to alcohol use • develop advertising tactics for promoting healthy alternatives
Setting Personal Goals for NOT Using Alcohol	• identify reasons why they personally don't want to use alcohol	• establish short-term goals for staying alcohol free
Role of Parents, Guardians, and the Community in Preventing Teen Alcohol Use	• discuss alcohol use with their parents/guardians • discuss their family's expectations about alcohol use	• describe an adult's perspective on the negative consequences of alcohol use

continued on next page

Duplicating this material for personal or group use is permissible.

Project Northland Scope and Sequence

TOPIC	POWER LINES (8th Grade)	CLASS ACTION (9–12th Grade)
Students will demonstrate the ability to:		
Facts about Alcohol	• review alternatives to underage drinking • review consequences of underage drinking	• describe laws and policies that regulate underage alcohol use • describe laws and policies that hold individuals within a community responsible for underage alcohol use • know basic facts about alcohol and its effect on the human body • know that teen alcohol use is an extremely risky choice
Reasons for Alcohol Use	• examine community influences on teen alcohol use	• weigh reasons to use against potential for harm
Consequences of Alcohol Use	• review negative consequences that show why an eighth grader should not use alcohol • review consequences of underage drinking • examine and discuss influences, consequences, and responsibilities related to underage drinking • identify individual and community consequences of teen alcohol use	• identify how a teen's alcohol use can affect his or her family, friends, and others in the community • identify personal consequences (physical, emotional, social) of teen alcohol use • identify the legal consequences of teen alcohol use • describe how alcohol affects a person's driving ability, a developing fetus, dating relationships, and tendencies toward violence
Peer Pressure and Alcohol Use	• review refusal skills	• realize the personal responsibility teens have to stay sober • accurately weigh the pressure to use versus the potential harm from using alcohol
Evaluating Alcohol Advertisements	• review ways that advertisers try to influence teen alcohol use	
Finding Positive Alternatives to Alcohol	• review alternatives to underage drinking • identify ways that eighth graders can positively influence their community's underage drinking issues	• identify positive alternatives to alcohol use • identify alternatives that a community could choose to prevent teen alcohol use
Setting Personal Goals for NOT Using Alcohol	• review the goals they set for themselves last year • set goals to remain alcohol free	• realize the personal responsibility every teen has to stay sober • choose to refuse alcohol
Role of Parents, Guardians, and the Community in Preventing Teen Alcohol Use	• define "community" and "influence" • examine community influences on teen alcohol use • examine ways that teens influence their community • examine different perspectives on underage drinking • outline, propose, and select community strategies to prevent teen alcohol use • examine alcohol-related laws, policies, resources, and influences in their own community	• identify how teen alcohol use affects others in the community • identify teen alcohol use as a community-wide problem • describe laws and policies that have been developed to prevent teens from using alcohol

For a printable version of this chart, see the CD-ROM. Also, see the CD-ROM for detailed session descriptions with preparation needed for each curriculum.

     Duplicating this material for personal or group use is permissible.

Meeting National Academic Standards with Project Northland

Using Project Northland will help you meet these national academic standards, reprinted here with permission:[21]

Health Education

Students will

- understand how various messages from the media, peers, and other sources impact health practices

- know influences that promote alcohol, tobacco, and other drug use

- know strategies for resisting negative peer pressure

- know ways to recognize, avoid, and respond to negative social influences and pressure to use alcohol, tobacco, and other drugs

- know strategies to manage stress and difficult feelings

- know appropriate ways to build and maintain positive relationships with peers, parents, and other adults

- know safety rules and practices to be used in home, school, and community settings

- know changes that occur during puberty

- know the short- and long-term consequences of the use of alcohol, tobacco, and other drugs

- know community resources that are available to assist people with alcohol, tobacco, and other drug problems

English/Language Arts

WRITING

Students will

- use general skills and strategies of the writing process

- gather and use information for research purposes

- use a variety of resource materials to gather information for research topics

- organize information and ideas from multiple sources in systematic ways

---

Content Knowledge: A Compendium of Standards and Benchmarks for K–12 Education is the copyrighted work of McREL, http://www.mcrel.org/standards-benchmarks, 303-337-0990.

READING

Students will

- establish and adjust purposes for reading

- reflect on what has been learned after reading and formulate ideas, opinions, and personal responses to text

- use reading skills and strategies to understand and interpret a variety of informational texts

- use new information to adjust and extend personal knowledge base

- draw conclusions and make inferences based on explicit and implicit information in texts

LISTENING AND SPEAKING

Students will

- contribute to group discussions

- play a variety of roles in group discussions

- ask questions to seek elaboration and clarification of ideas

- use strategies to enhance listening comprehension

- listen to and understand persuasive messages

- understand elements of persuasion

- respond to questions and comments

VIEWING AND MEDIA

Students will

- use viewing skills and strategies to understand and interpret visual media

- understand basic elements of advertising in visual media

- understand how symbols, images, sound, and other conventions are used in visual media

- know that people with special interests and expectations are the target audience for particular messages or products in visual media

---

Content Knowledge: A Compendium of Standards and Benchmarks for K–12 Education is the copyrighted work of McREL, http://www.mcrel.org/standards-benchmarks, 303-337-0990.

Duplicating this material for curriculum planning is permissible.

- understand techniques used in visual media to influence or appeal to a particular audience

- know that a variety of people are involved in creating media messages and products

- understand the different purposes of various media

- understand ways in which image makers carefully construct meaning

- understand influences on the construction of media messages and images

Civics

Students will

- know ways people can influence the decisions and actions of their government

- know individuals or groups who monitor and influence the decisions and actions of local, state, tribal, and national governments

Life Skills

THINKING AND REASONING

Students will

- use facts from books, articles, and databases to support an argument

- make basic distinctions between information that is based on fact and information that is based on opinion

- know how personal health can be influenced by society

- analyze problems that have confronted people in the past

- generate alternative courses of action and compare the possible consequences of alternatives

- select the most appropriate strategy or alternative for solving a problem

- identify situations in the community and in one's personal life in which a decision is required

---

Content Knowledge: A Compendium of Standards and Benchmarks for K–12 Education is the copyrighted work of McREL, http://www.mcrel.org/standards-benchmarks, 303-337-0990.

- secure factual information needed to evaluate alternatives and use it to predict the consequences of selecting each alternative
- take action to implement a decision, monitor progress, and adjust when needed

WORKING WITH OTHERS

Students will

- contribute to the overall efforts of a group
- display effective interpersonal communication skills
- demonstrate leadership skills

SELF-REGULATION

Students will

- set and manage goals
- consider risks
- demonstrate perseverance
- restrain impulsivity

 For a printable version of this list, see the CD-ROM.

• • •

Content Knowledge: A Compendium of Standards and Benchmarks for K–12 Education is the copyrighted work of McREL, http://www.mcrel.org/standards-benchmarks, 303-337-0990.

Duplicating this material for curriculum planning is permissible.

Responsibilities of the Project Northland Coordinator

A great program coordinator is often the key to successful Project Northland implementation. One may share this role with another person, especially if time is limited. There are many people—teachers, school administrators, parents and guardians, local business owners, health care providers, safety officers, and the students themselves—who share a stake in the success of this program, so let others share in the work and the responsibility, too.

▶▶ *What You Will Learn in Chapter 2:*

- What is the benefit of having a Project Northland coordinator?
- What are important qualities in a Project Northland coordinator?
- What does a Project Northland coordinator do?
- What should a Project Northland coordinator learn before implementation?

What Is the Benefit of Having a Project Northland Coordinator?

Not every Project Northland implementation site has a full-time coordinator. A group of people may share coordination responsibilities as a team. Part-time coordinators may help implement Project Northland as part of another position. There may be a coordinator who supports several sites, with a Project Northland liaison at each site. All of these models may be successful.

There are, however, tremendous benefits to having a full-time Project Northland coordinator on site to manage the entire project as his or her primary responsibility, without other teaching or administrative responsibilities. This person is fully dedicated to the program's success. This kind of program coordinator can more clearly see the big picture and fit all its pieces together to make a complete whole.

Duplicating this page is illegal. Do not copy this material without written permission from the publisher.

Coordinators often train Peer Leaders, freeing other staff from that responsibility. They organize Poster Fairs, prepare materials, and build networks of resources. Coordinating schedules and ensuring adequate communication between teachers, with parents and guardians, and with media and the community all are among the tasks performed best by a coordinator.

You may select a school counselor, school administrator, prevention specialist, teacher, member of the nonteaching staff, or parent/guardian volunteer to be your Project Northland coordinator. Depending upon the number of students or schools involved, this could also be a full-time paid position.

What Are Important Qualities in a Project Northland Coordinator?

It is important that the Project Northland coordinator

- has good leadership and communication skills

- has the support of the school and district administration

- is organized

- is a good communicator

- is a good facilitator

- has good listening skills

- is able to work well with school administrators, staff, faculty, and parents and guardians, and is someone school personnel respect

- is able to work well with diverse groups and coalitions

- is permitted by the administration to devote adequate time to program coordination

- feels passionate about the issue of alcohol-use prevention

- is familiar with Project Northland and is an advocate of the program

- is available to attend Project Northland training and to facilitate the training of other staff

PROFESSIONAL HIGHLIGHT

"Our Safe and Drug-Free Schools coordinators are our Project Northland coordinators. Most are county public health. There's one family center and one school district. One county attorney general's office is involved, too."

CHEMICAL HEALTH DIVISION PLANNER, STATE DEPARTMENT OF HUMAN SERVICES (MINNESOTA)

Duplicating this page is illegal. Do not copy this material without written permission from the publisher.

It is also helpful for the Project Northland coordinator to

- have a basic understanding of community change processes

- have effective management experience

 PROGRAM TIP

What Additional Training Might Be Useful to a Project Northland Coordinator?
Particularly for coordinators who are school-based personnel, community organizer training may be useful. During the authors' work, community organizers received training in six key areas: one-on-one interviews, community mobilizing, building a campaign around youth access initiatives, action team building, thinking strategically and politically, and policies and ordinances. A significant part of the training helped organizers develop the skill to conduct one-on-one interviews as a means of engaging the community.

What Does a Project Northland Coordinator Do?

Project Northland coordinators assume a variety of roles:

- ■ **The Curriculum Expert:** The coordinator's most important role is as the community's expert on Project Northland. Here are some ways to perform this task before, during, and after implementation:

Before the project starts:

- View the DVD program overview.

- Read this manual thoroughly.

- Familiarize yourself with the resources available on the CD-ROM.

- Read each curriculum: *Slick Tracy, Amazing Alternatives, Power Lines,* and *Class Action.*

- Page through the *Slick Tracy* comic books.

During Project Northland implementation:

- Help prepare materials for classroom use.

- Keep in touch with those teaching the curricula.

- Attend—and probably coordinate—poster nights and events.

- Observe lessons in the classroom.

Duplicating this page is illegal. Do not copy this material without written permission from the publisher.

After curriculum implementation:

- Talk with students and teachers about their experiences, learning, and suggestions for program improvement.

- Collect their questions and follow up with answers.

- Review any evaluations and correspondence.

- Request any items needed from Hazelden.

■ **Go-To Person:** You will be the best person to problem-solve and answer questions for people working directly with students. Build connections with others who have more experience using Project Northland—including teachers, coordinators, and trainers—so you can call on them for help as needed.

■ **Fellow Learner:** Position yourself as one learner within a community of learners. It is important to remember that you do not need to know all the answers before you begin. It would be quite an accomplishment even to know all the questions! You will continue to learn throughout the process from many people and milestones you will encounter.

It may help to recognize your own personal and professional strengths, such as an understanding of curriculum or an ability to motivate others. When you are aware of what you bring to the community, you are better able to offer it. Similarly, when you recognize the strengths of others, such as relating to their students or knowing the needs of a particular age group, you are more receptive to learning from them.

■ **Program Promoter and Publicity Manager:** Spread the word about Project Northland in meetings, by phone, by e-mail, and by other available means. Seize and create opportunities to connect with teachers, administrators, parent and teacher organizations, counselors, school boards, and others. Establish contact with local newspapers and other media to spread the word about the new curriculum and its benefits and events in

Duplicating this page is illegal. Do not copy this material without written permission from the publisher.

PROGRAM TIP

What Are Project Northland's Curricula?

The best preparation for coordinating Project Northland is reading the curriculum itself, taking time to study the introductory pieces and to get a good sense of the activities for each grade level. There are three middle school curricula and a high school program, described on pages 7–9 in chapter 1. The table below summarizes key features of each curriculum:

	SLICK TRACY	AMAZING ALTERNATIVES	POWER LINES	CLASS ACTION
Curriculum focus	Families communicating a no-use message about alcohol use	Peers and social norms	Community influences and social norms	Legal consequences of harm done by underage alcohol use
Designed for	Sixth grade	Seventh grade	Eighth grade	Tenth or eleventh grade
Local needs analysis may indicate appropriate use with	Fifth or sixth grade	Seventh grade only	Eighth grade only	Twelfth grade *(Note: One case may be used as a model with ninth graders in a whole class setting to prepare them for group work later in high school.)*
Program highlights	• Activity/ comic books • Peer Leaders • Poster Fair	• Audio drama • Peer Leaders	• Franklin community meeting • Community research projects	Student teams receive evidence and prepare to prosecute
Special event/s	Poster Fair	*Amazing Alternatives* Fun Night/s are recommended	Project presentations	Mock trials
Peer Leaders	Nominated and trained	Nominated and trained	Shared leadership	Shared leadership
Notes	Send all four weekly comic books home with each student. Be sure to leave at least a week between each. Students may participate in Alternatives group.	This is the recommended grade level to lead a Student Alternatives group for planning and organizing alcohol-free social events.	Students interview community members. Students may participate in Alternatives group.	Use as a booster at least once during the high school years.

Duplicating this page is illegal. Do not copy this material without written permission from the publisher.

your community. Detailed ideas and suggestions regarding promotion and related communications are in chapter 9 and the accompanying CD-ROM materials.

■ **Funding Coordinator:** As the Project Northland administrator in your community, you may apply for grants and other financial support for the program. Funding information and resources are in chapter 4 and the accompanying CD-ROM materials.

■ **Training Coordinator:** You will want to make sure that all the necessary training takes place. Information and resources for this are in chapters 5 and 6 and the accompanying CD-ROM materials. Consider your own learning curve when you plan for staff training. Peer Leader training is also essential, and it is recommended that you train these students yourself.

■ **Implementation Coordinator:** You will orchestrate how Project Northland is rolled out in your community. You will make everything come together so that the program is used well. Information and resources to help are in chapter 5 and the accompanying CD-ROM materials.

■ **Program Evaluator:** Coordinate evaluation of your community's Project Northland program. You may perform the evaluation work yourself, or you may hire an outside evaluator who can provide the objectivity and expertise that funders may require. The evaluation process will allow your community to learn from experience. It will be an important step to continuous improvement. Information and resources for this role are in chapter 10 and the accompanying CD-ROM materials.

■ **Cheerleader and Guardian Angel:** You are the community's Project Northland representative. Help encourage, troubleshoot, hand-hold, model, train, organize the Poster Fair and other events, and celebrate the program and those involved.

Duplicating this page is illegal. Do not copy this material without written permission from the publisher.

Related information and resources are in chapter 6 and the accompanying CD-ROM materials.

■ **Community Mobilizer:** Kick-starting communitywide efforts to change youth alcohol-use behaviors will greatly benefit your implementation. Connect groups of people with each other. Bring families and community groups together to work toward common goals. Information and resources for community networking and coalition building are in chapter 8 and the accompanying CD-ROM materials.

Is the Project Northland Coordinator Expected to Do Everything?

There is no need for a program coordinator to do this work alone. You will want to connect with others, such as school counselors, community members, or interested teachers, to gather support for your work. An important goal of Project Northland is to bring communities together to improve the lives of all residents. The program may be taught in schools, but it belongs to everyone.

Many people have an important stake in the success of your program. Schools, community leaders, businesses, parents, and young people themselves all stand to gain. Successful implementation depends upon a concerted effort made by many people. Enlisting others' help and delegating responsibilities will help make sure that everyone remembers to do their part. It will also make your job, and the overall implementation, more successful.

It helps to develop champions within school sites. Such champions can support and promote the program among their peers and help divvy up some of the responsibilities. They can help train and inspire others.

What If Teachers Are Not Eager to Participate?

Experience has shown that once teachers are trained, they are excited to teach these curricula. Be sure to inform them of training requirements well in advance, to build appropriate expectations

PROGRAM TIP

When scheduling events, be sure to select times when families and community members are available to attend.

Duplicating this page is illegal. Do not copy this material without written permission from the publisher.

PROFESSIONAL HIGHLIGHT

"At first, the teachers all say, 'We're already teaching that. We have [a different program].' Once they get to know Project Northland and how well done it is, they get on board."

CHEMICAL HEALTH DIVISION PLANNER, STATE DEPARTMENT OF HUMAN SERVICES (MINNESOTA)

and enthusiasm. Help teachers realize what Project Northland offers to them. No one wants to educate and assist students more than their teachers do. When they understand that reducing and preventing alcohol use improves both learning and attendance, and when they realize that Project Northland really works, teachers will be more willing to devote precious time to it.

What If the Project Northland Coordinator Is Not a School Staff Person?

It is not necessary for the Project Northland coordinator to be employed by a school district or trained as a teacher. While some coordinators are school staff, many are based at prevention resource centers, educational service centers, county health departments, and community coalitions. Whoever you are, whether you have been chosen for this position or volunteered for it, this manual has been written to help you to succeed.

What Resources Are Available for Support?

There are extensive resources in this manual, on the accompanying CD-ROM, and on the DVD. The CD-ROM also offers several lists of additional resources. You will also want to identify supporters within your community. To ensure fidelity of implementation, Hazelden recommends professional training and offers several training options. See chapter 4 for funding ideas that can help pay for training and materials and chapter 5 for more information about Project Northland training.

What Else Do I Need to Determine Before Getting Started?

It will be useful to know your budget and timeline for implementing the program. It will also help if you know how many students and educators will be included, so you can figure out how many sets of program materials to order. On the CD-ROM, there are resources that can help you organize and plan, including an implementation worksheet and sample logic models.

Duplicating this page is illegal. Do not copy this material without written permission from the publisher.

Summary

Project Northland coordinators wear many hats. Your program can run without a full-time, dedicated coordinator, but you can expect it to be easier, more effective, and more sustainable if one person is dedicated to developing the expertise to fully oversee these responsibilities. Familiarizing yourself with the program, building community connections, and identifying your champions will benefit your work.

∘   ∘   ∘

Duplicating this page is illegal. Do not copy this material without written permission from the publisher.

CHAPTER 3

Bringing Project Northland to Your Community

Every community is unique. This chapter will help you identify the defining characteristics, challenges, and strengths of your community and help you build a successful Project Northland program based upon your community's strengths. At the earliest stages of implementation, you can begin creating a sustainable infrastructure by gaining the support of school and district leadership, building community interest, and incorporating community readiness strategies from this chapter.

▶▶ *What You Will Learn in Chapter 3:*

- How do communities begin Project Northland implementation?
- What are the defining characteristics of my community?
- Why is Project Northland's environmental approach better than a standard curriculum?
- What is the importance of Project Northland's fidelity guidelines?
- What are the challenges of implementing Project Northland?
- Why is community readiness important?

How Do Communities Begin Project Northland Implementation?

The organizations that bring Project Northland to different communities vary. In some cases, regional prevention centers or education service centers may do the work of researching and selecting the program, as well as of securing funds. In others, school districts may handle these responsibilities internally. Community coalitions have been strong advocates leading Project Northland implementations, and some juvenile justice systems lead implementation in their areas. Although program delivery is in schools, program coordination and support may come from any of these sources, or others. As public awareness and concern about underage drinking and other youth issues increase, many other types of organizations may become involved.

Duplicating this page is illegal. Do not copy this material without written permission from the publisher.

31

PROFESSIONAL HIGHLIGHT

"University of Rhode Island researchers compared Project Northland with two other alcohol-use prevention programs. In their conclusions, they state: 'If the goal is decreasing initiation of use (any experimentation with alcohol), Project Northland is a more promising choice, especially for nonwhite and lower S.E.S. students.'"

COMMUNITY RESEARCH AND SERVICES TEAM AT THE UNIVERSITY OF RHODE ISLAND

PROFESSIONAL HIGHLIGHT

Community Anti-Drug Coalitions of America (CADCA) sponsors "Got Outcomes!" a competitive awards program designed to acknowledge coalitions that implement evidence-based multiple strategies to achieve a community-wide outcome. Award recipients include Project Northland implementers in eastern Kentucky and in Vermont.

Has Project Northland Been Used in Diverse Communities?

Project Northland has been used effectively all over the United States and in several other countries. The communities using it have been urban, suburban, and rural, with populations both diverse and fairly homogeneous. The communities have been at all points along the economic spectrum. Some have had teachers deliver the curricula. Others have employed health educators, program coordinators, and others in this capacity. Project Northland has succeeded in this wide variety of settings.

You can implement Project Northland successfully in your community, too. To begin:

- Identify the key characteristics of your community and determine how you can meet community-specific challenges by drawing on the community's strengths.

- Understand the key parts of the program that must be implemented as written, and know which parts you may adapt.

Building cultural competence into implementation enhances the success of any program. This involves considering the range of cultural influences that interact in your community and how best to include these in your program. Culturally competent organizations and programs are more current, more effective, more inclusive, and more sustainable. The Nebraska Partners in Prevention Web site (http://www.nebraskaprevention.gov/CCEP .htm) provides guidelines for prevention efforts. Information about these, and other resources to help build cultural competency, may be found on the CD-ROM.

What Are the Defining Characteristics of My Community?

These are defining characteristics to consider:

- community size and type (rural, urban, or suburban)

- diversity and culture, including language, ethnicity, and religion

Duplicating this page is illegal. Do not copy this material without written permission from the publisher.

- constituents and resources, including leaders, businesses, schools, law enforcement, coalitions, youth-serving organizations, health professionals, government, special populations, and more

- strengths—Which resources will form your strongest initial base of support?

- challenges—Which resources will you want to develop over time?

- perceptions—Is alcohol use by youth perceived as a primary problem?

- readiness—Is there an openness and a readiness to make prevention of underage drinking a priority of the community?

You probably possess most or all of this information without doing any research. Pieces you may not know can be learned fairly easily. Still, it is useful to document and organize the facts. Then the information will be handy for you to use throughout Project Northland implementation. This is especially handy when writing grant applications and working on community mobilization.

Ideas about how coalitions can help with community assessment and capacity building are in chapter 8. Communities That Care (CTC) and Community Anti-Drug Coalitions of America (CADCA) provide additional community assessment resources, and their contact information is on the CD-ROM. A Community Assessment Worksheet is also available on the CD-ROM. If you choose to use this resource, be sure to add your own notes, questions, and ideas. If you work with more than one community, you may use a separate copy of this worksheet to assess each one.

Parts of the Community Assessment Worksheet include space for you to summarize your findings in a sentence or two. Writing these as you work through the checklist, you will prepare material for several paragraphs describing your community demographically, geographically, and in terms of potential challenges and strengths. Remember to revisit this document periodically as you continue to gather information. Having a

Duplicating this page is illegal. Do not copy this material without written permission from the publisher.

clear, complete, and current description of your community will help you apply for funding and plan for a strong, well-organized communitywide implementation of Project Northland.

 PROGRAM TIP

Does Your Community Have an Existing Coalition?
You can contact Community Anti-Drug Coalitions of America (CADCA) to find out. Also, you can request free resources from CADCA, like the Environmental Prevention Strategies booklet and the Primer series. Primer topics include community assessment, planning, capacity building, cultural competence, implementation, evaluation, and sustainability. CADCA also offers online resources and e-mail updates.

Why Is Project Northland's Environmental Approach Better Than a Standard Curriculum?

Addressing the multiple domains of family, peers, school, community, and society, Project Northland was one of the first of what are now commonly called "environmental" prevention programs. Environmental prevention aims to make the community environment less conducive to alcohol use. Based on the public health model, the environmental approach recognizes and works with key aspects of community that can make it either easier and more acceptable, or harder and less acceptable, for teens to obtain and drink alcohol.

It addresses policies and practices like the following:

- minimum drinking age laws
- zero tolerance, DUI, and DWI laws
- consistent enforcement of existing laws
- restrictions upon location of liquor stores and bars
- registration requirements for kegs
- compliance checks regarding age-of-purchase laws
- accountability for adults who provide alcohol to minors
- restrictions upon alcohol available at community events
- promotion of alcohol-free events
- Responsible Beverage Service training

Duplicating this page is illegal. Do not copy this material without written permission from the publisher.

- restrictions on promotion of community events by alcohol companies

- community education

- media advocacy

- workplace programs

- increasing taxes on alcohol

- requiring license fees of alcohol providers

- mobilizing communities to support youth development

 PROFESSIONAL HIGHLIGHT

CASE EXAMPLE 1

**Two Coalitions—One Experienced and One Novice—
Drive Neighboring Implementations**

In northwestern Oregon, two rural towns began implementing Project Northland in 1999. In one, a strong coalition had existed for several years. It was this coalition that had selected Project Northland for their middle school. In the other town, Project Northland adoption was the first strategy selected to address higher-than-average underage alcohol use.

Working with the county prevention program, the coalitions applied a three-phase model in each community. Year 1, the coalition's prevention specialist delivered Project Northland to sixth-grade classrooms while the teachers observed. Year 2, the prevention specialist and sixth-grade classroom teachers collaborated, often as a tag team, to carry out Peer Leader training, classroom delivery, and student support. Year 3, the prevention specialist had a minimal role providing support for the classroom teacher. This model was introduced for seventh grade during year 2 and for eighth grade during year 3.

The community with the older coalition was quick out of the gate and adopted an aggressive implementation model introducing both sixth- and seventh-grade curricula in year 1. However, their efforts were challenged when school staff demonstrated difficulty accepting the program. While the coalition had a long history in the community, members of the school staff were unfamiliar with it and felt that their own input was not valued. Members of the coalition believed they knew what was best based on data and research, whereas school staff thought they knew

what was best because they knew the students. The conflict could be traced back to rushing implementation and neglecting to create buy-in by taking the time needed to develop and nurture relationships with important stakeholders—the classroom teachers—before and throughout implementation.

In the community that started a new coalition when they adopted Project Northland, all parties went through the learning process together. Community leaders, educators, parents, and youth were all involved, and all were gathering information at the same time. As a result, there were fewer turf issues, and the program was sustained by the school without county funding at the end of the grant term. When this coalition evolved and redefined its efforts, Project Northland had laid a foundation for larger K–12 prevention efforts.

Both programs—the one with a preexisting coalition and the one that built its coalition alongside Project Northland adoption—have been successful and sustainable. The experienced coalition implemented Project Northland more quickly and surely, but it ran into difficulties because its leadership by well-intentioned and highly driven members was initially positioned in a way that created conflict with highly committed teachers who had clear ideas and substantial experience with students and curricula. The newer coalition seemed to experience a more harmonious process because everyone came at the project on equal ground.

Duplicating this page is illegal. Do not copy this material without written permission from the publisher.

Because much human behavior is socially determined, environmental prevention is thought to be more successful than prevention that merely educates the individual. For this reason, community involvement can greatly enhance the outcomes of your Project Northland program.

More information and ideas about community involvement and coalition building may be found in chapter 8.

What Is the Importance of Project Northland's Fidelity Guidelines?

Project Northland is an evidence-based program, built upon years of research about what makes alcohol prevention effective. In order to use the program effectively and achieve significant outcomes, it is important to implement the program with fidelity. This means the program should be implemented by your community in a way that is as close as possible to it's implementation during the authors' study. There are key aspects of the original program that must be maintained in order to achieve the desired results. These include but are not limited to parent and community involvement, peer leadership, and implementation of the complete curricula, including Time Capsules and the *Slick Tracy* Poster Fair.

 PROFESSIONAL HIGHLIGHT

CASE EXAMPLE 2

Fidelity of Implementation Serves ROE's Wide-Ranging Schools for More Than a Decade

One midwestern regional office of education (ROE) implements Project Northland in two counties with thirty-nine schools across a large geographic area. The student composition of the area's schools ranges ethnically from nearly all black to nearly all white, with a sizable Spanish-speaking Latino population at several schools. Due to the level of student mobility between the area's schools, district leadership wanted a consistent health education program.

Project Northland was selected to address underage alcohol use because—while the same effective lessons would be delivered across the counties—each curriculum includes school, family, and community outreach activities that could be customized at the local level to best meet each community's needs and utilize its resources. Implementation leaders found that only the most minimal adaptations were needed to meet the needs of the region's students and their families. For example, Spanish-speaking students present their *Slick Tracy* Poster Fair projects in Spanish to Spanish-speaking adults.

This region has been able to boast excellent outcomes based on more than ten years of local data collection. According to the program director, a greater nondrinking norm exists among participating students than the national average—63.4 percent for program participants, 52.5 percent for local counterparts, and 58.2 percent for the peer group nationally. Locally, Project Northland participants are 26 percent more likely to have friends who never use alcohol and 31 percent more likely to have friends who disapprove of drinking. Participants are 19 percent more likely to indicate that their parents talked to them often or a lot about problems related to alcohol use. Also, participating students are 18 percent to 25 percent less likely than their local counterparts to have smoked cigarettes in the past year or on a monthly basis. These successes are not merely equaled by students of color; the data for these students surpass the county population as a whole.

Duplicating this page is illegal. Do not copy this material without written permission from the publisher.

That said, each community is unique, and tailoring the program to meet local needs is encouraged. For instance, it is fine to incorporate volunteer "judges" for the *Slick Tracy* Poster Fair. It is fine to read the *Amazing Alternatives* scripts aloud rather than listen to the recordings. Program materials may be read aloud as needed for low-proficiency readers. You may add program components, adjust the timing of lesson delivery, and change names and locations in the stories to have them better correspond to your community. Special family and community events should reflect local flavors and interests.

The following list explains which components are essential in order to achieve the excellent results that Project Northland implementation has brought in other communities. Replication studies show that—even in communities quite different from those where the program was piloted—faithful program implementation yields strong results. These elements of the program are essential to ensure fidelity and success:

▪ **All three middle school grade levels should be taught to all the students.** Students need to hear a consistent prevention message over several years to achieve positive outcomes. *Slick Tracy, Amazing Alternatives,* and *Power Lines* are sequential. Each builds to the next and presents key concepts in developmentally appropriate ways, and all three are important.

▪ **Focus on ALCOHOL prevention while teaching Project Northland.** Do not modify activities to focus on other drugs, as this may affect outcomes. However, talking about other drugs during class is natural and encouraged. Project Northland has been shown to effectively prevent other drug use, but its intent is to prevent alcohol use. Alcohol is the drug most widely used by teens, and it is often a "gateway" to other drug use, so focusing efforts to reduce underage alcohol use has multiple benefits.

▪ **Teach all of the lessons in each curriculum.**

RESEARCH FACT

In the authors' Chicago study, secondary outcome analyses to assess the effectiveness of each program component indicated that the home-based pieces were associated with reduced alcohol, marijuana, and tobacco use.[1]

Duplicating this page is illegal. Do not copy this material without written permission from the publisher.

PROFESSIONAL HIGHLIGHT

"I had five teachers with no experience teaching the program and they all liked it. They liked it, and they were successful."

ADMINISTRATOR
(ALABAMA)

3a

Complete fidelity guidelines are included on the CD-ROM.

■ **Peer Leaders, not adults, must deliver all activities specified as peer led.** Prevention research shows that peers serve as more effective sources of socially based information and key role models for positive social behaviors. It is important to train Peer Leaders effectively.

■ **Students, not adults, must choose the Peer Leaders.**

■ **Send home the *Slick Tracy* comic books and all other family materials, including letters and flyers, for each curriculum.** Prevention research shows that parent or guardian involvement promotes and sustains positive behavior in young people. Family participation and communication are essential.

■ **Connect as many students as possible with adults for Home Team participation.** The expectation is for each student to complete the Home Team activities outside of school with a caring and supportive adult.

■ **Integrate Project Northland with communitywide efforts to prevent underage alcohol use.** During the original study, Project Northland was implemented in communities with adult coalitions and youth groups that had made alcohol-use prevention a priority. While the curricula do explore community issues, prevention efforts on the community level are necessary to change environmental risk factors.

■ **Teacher training is necessary.** The success of the program is directly related to how faithfully it is implemented in the classroom. Training enhances fidelity.

■ **If coalitions are involved, it is necessary to train the coalition members, too.** With the focus on changing community norms and policies regarding youth access to alcohol, members of existing coalitions need to be trained and brought in to support Project Northland.

Duplicating this page is illegal. Do not copy this material without written permission from the publisher.

What Are the Challenges of Implementing Project Northland?

- It is important to gain the support of key leaders, especially school district leaders and building administrators. These people can facilitate your efforts in many ways.

- It is essential to establish that teachers who will deliver the curricula value the program. Leadership can help pave the way, but you must ensure that you have teacher buy-in.

PROFESSIONAL HIGHLIGHT

"We used [a different program] before. Teachers weren't getting the results that they wanted, and they found it dry and stale."

SAFE AND DRUG-FREE SCHOOLS
PROGRAM COORDINATOR
(NORTH CAROLINA)

 PROFESSIONAL HIGHLIGHT

CASE EXAMPLE 3

Fidelity Improvements and Fun Incentives Strengthen Outcomes

In the Midwest, a well-funded suburban school district of about 10,000 students began implementing Project Northland. Unfortunately, the program did not start with good buy-in from teachers, and teachers generally did not implement the curricula with fidelity. After two years, the school district restarted implementation, requiring improved fidelity and greater support for all three middle school grades.

This time, teachers reported good parent participation at the sixth-grade level. *Slick Tracy* Poster Fair participation was boosted with a competition awarding a pizza party to the class with the highest level of parent attendance. Also, students' posters were displayed in the community after the Poster Fair. *Amazing Alternatives* and *Power Lines* were both implemented with rigorous attention to program guidelines. Teachers and community members were impressed with the high quality of students' community projects. Students reported that they learned a lot and were proud of their work.

Every three years, the school district surveys students for risk behaviors and attitudes. Three years after implementing the program improvements, sixth and ninth graders reported significantly less alcohol use. Seventy-nine percent of ninth-grade males and 70 percent of ninth-grade females reported no alcohol use over the last twelve months, as opposed to only 66

percent and 59 percent three years earlier. During the last thirty days, 89 percent of males and 81 percent of females reported no use, compared to 78 percent and 75 percent before. Also, 90 percent of students who had completed Project Northland demonstrated an understanding that binge drinking puts people at risk of serious harm.

The school district's survey data indicate that students' increased awareness of the risks of alcohol use, and their decreased use of it, are tied to Project Northland's use in schools. Eighty-five percent of sixth graders and 71 percent of ninth graders reported that they received most of their information about alcohol and drugs from teachers and counselors in school.

This school district's story illustrates several points:

- Project Northland is most successful in achieving strong outcomes when the program is implemented with fidelity.

- Participation and parent engagement can be increased with simple, low-cost adjustments, such as adding the pizza competition.

- Community awareness and support can be gained at minimal cost by displaying posters and sharing projects in the larger community.

Duplicating this page is illegal. Do not copy this material without written permission from the publisher.

- If you do not have a staff person dedicated to coordinating Project Northland, implementation will be more challenging. Chapter 2 discusses the role of a program coordinator and the benefits of having one.

- Funding will be needed for materials, training, and support. See chapter 4 for funding tips and ideas.

- The community's level of readiness, discussed below, will impact the effectiveness of implementation.

- The community may not perceive an underage drinking problem. The needs analysis process discussed in chapter 4 can help you clarify this issue and identify key data that will help others understand the local issue.

- If the community has already tried a different alcohol-use prevention program that is not as effective or engaging as Project Northland, people may be skeptical until they learn about the significant benefits unique to Project Northland.

Why Is Community Readiness Important?

A community that is invested in preventing underage drinking and ready to embrace Project Northland's effective environmental approach will help your program succeed. Community readiness is an important ingredient for the success of any prevention program. You know your community is ready for Project Northland when the following occur:

- School and district leadership make a commitment.

- A base of community interest, support, and/or awareness exists around the need for alcohol prevention.

- The majority of administrators and educators value alcohol prevention.

- Funding is available for materials, training, and ongoing support.

- You have a few champions at key sites who believe in the program and will support its use.

Duplicating this page is illegal. Do not copy this material without written permission from the publisher.

• You have a commitment from the implementation sites, the community, and funders for long-term implementation.

• You have talked through the program with a certified Project Northland trainer and/or attended training in order to clearly understand the program.

If the community is ready, build upon the positive interest that exists to create even more receptiveness and inclusiveness. If your community does not seem ready to make alcohol-use prevention a priority, you may be able to help with this.

What Can I Do to Help My Community Become Ready?

You can raise the community's level of readiness by alerting community members to the facts about underage alcohol use, including the risks it poses to the community. You can further educate people about the corresponding benefits offered by Project Northland's effective alcohol-use prevention program. Fact sheets directed to various stakeholders are included on the CD-ROM. You may particularly want to educate school leadership, parents or guardians, and community groups about how Project Northland can help meet their needs.

These ideas are adapted from the Community Readiness Model strategies developed and tested at Colorado State University:[2]

• Inform people about the issue using both general information and specific local incidents and statistics.

• Approach and engage local education and health outreach programs, enlisting their help with flyers, posters, brochures, or other publicity efforts.

• Send press releases to local newspapers and bulletins, community and school newsletters, and Web sites. Include both general trends and specific local information. Highlight any related incidents that have been in the news.

Duplicating this page is illegal. Do not copy this material without written permission from the publisher.

- Present information at local events, perhaps at a booth where people can go to get information, take an awareness quiz, and so on.

- Conduct informal local surveys, either in person or by phone.

Assessing and developing community readiness will help you sustain Project Northland over time to benefit thousands of learners. The Community Assessment Worksheet on the CD-ROM can help, and online resources offer more information to help guide your community to readiness. A selection of these resources is included on the CD-ROM that accompanies this manual.

 PROGRAM TIP

Interviewing as a Bridge to the Community

You may find one-on-one interviewing to be a useful technique both for building your base of support and for getting to know community members. During the authors' implementation, community organizers interviewed citizens who represented a broad spectrum of the community—faith organizations, businesses, liquor merchants, medical organizations, educational organizations, and so on—and who had an interest in the prevention of adolescent alcohol use. These interviews were designed to build a broad base, encourage recognition of the interviewees' interests, and identify the community's social, economic, and political power structures. You might consider organizing a task force to help conduct similar interviews in your community.

Summary

It is important to lay groundwork for any new initiative. Project Northland is designed as a communitywide program, so you might lay more groundwork for this than for a classroom-only program. Outcomes and sustainability make this effort well spent. While working on community readiness before curriculum implementation, consider how best to work with your unique community and identify its key resources.

·　·　·

Duplicating this page is illegal. Do not copy this material without written permission from the publisher.

CHAPTER 4

Funding Your Program

Implementing Project Northland, like any significant school or community initiative, requires funding to support staff, pay for training, and buy materials and related supplies. This chapter will help you identify your funding needs and identify strategies to meet those needs, including support from federal, state, and local government agencies; foundations; local businesses; charities; and philanthropic organizations.

▶▶ *What You Will Learn in Chapter 4:*

- What funding will be needed?
- Where can funds be obtained?
- What is the best way to write a grant proposal?

What Funding Will Be Needed?

Minimally, you will need funds for program materials and training. Ideally, you will acquire funds to support your efforts every step of the way—start-up, implementation, evaluation, and continuous improvement to sustain the program. Resources to help with budget planning are provided on the CD-ROM and in this manual, and their use is explained in this chapter. When you plan program funding, consider all of your budget needs:

■ **Staff:** Will a program coordinator be paid? How much will this cost in total salary and benefits? Will other program staff be paid, too?

■ **Materials:** Work with a Hazelden representative to determine how many sets of materials you will need. It is recommended for each teacher to receive a copy of the curriculum he or she will use. In addition, it is a good idea for each school's principal and curriculum director to have a full set of curricula, including this manual.

Duplicating this page is illegal. Do not copy this material without written permission from the publisher.

■ **Training:** It is highly recommended that schools contract for training to ensure fidelity of implementation. Hazelden representatives are available to help determine an appropriate training budget based on the size of the school or district and the scope of community involvement. Trainer fees, travel, lodging, and refreshments are usually part of the training budget. You might also consider space rental. You may have a trainer come to your community, or you can send staff members to an open-enrollment training at Hazelden.

Be sure to include any related staff costs in your training budget. If you can, schedule Project Northland training on a regular staff development day to avoid extra expenses. Otherwise, be sure to include funds to compensate teachers for their additional time, or include funds to pay reserve teachers to release teaching staff from their regular duties for training during the school day. Contact a Hazelden representative about budget questions.

■ **Special Events:** *Slick Tracy* has an evening Poster Fair, and it is recommended that implementation includes alcohol-free social alternatives for teens. You may also want to host a Community Launch Party, as described in chapter 5, to build enthusiasm and attract parents and guardians, educators, and community leaders. There are opportunities to create events around the *Power Lines* projects and *Class Action's* mock trials, too. Local businesses, including grocery stores and bakeries, may contribute refreshments for such events. If not, you will want to budget for this.

PROFESSIONAL HIGHLIGHT

"When I talk with kids at the Poster Fair, they express a lot of enjoyment."

COMMUNITY HEALTH PARTNERSHIP (MASSACHUSETTS)

■ **Incentives:** Incentives encourage participation. It is expected that incentives will be given to students who complete their Home Team assignments during *Slick Tracy,* and incentives may be used to motivate older students and adult participants, too. Will local businesses donate items that you can use? Will you purchase some with grant funds?

Do you plan to offer incentives for teachers who complete additional paperwork involved (such as signing off on the

Duplicating this page is illegal. Do not copy this material without written permission from the publisher.

Project Northland Scope and Sequence document, completing evaluation components and record keeping, or working with a coordinator on program fidelity)? If so, include these in your budget, too.

 PROGRAM TIP

Teacher participation may be more robust if you can offer monetary or other incentive rewards. One effective community offers each Project Northland teacher a $25 stipend per lesson for completing evaluation items and documenting fidelity. It may serve your program well to include incentives for participating teachers in your budget.

■ **Photocopies:** It is a good idea to estimate photocopying needs and budget for them.

■ **Mail, office supplies, and more:** Each curriculum has parent/ guardian letters that need to be sent home, as well as additional resources on the CD-ROM. You will also want resources to facilitate community outreach. Will you need a computer? Do you have a workspace? Do you need to budget for office supplies? How much mailing will you do, and how will that cost be covered? Are phone, voice mail, and e-mail services already available to facilitate your work, or do these need to be arranged?

■ **Evaluation:** Do you plan to hire an outside evaluator? What evaluation costs do you anticipate?

Your Total Budget

1. Come up with a reasonable budget range. Usually, this range depends on two things: the scope of your project and the average amounts that your selected granting agency has given in the past and/or intends to give this budget cycle. For example, if your state's department of education normally gives $50,000 to $80,000 grants in this category, and yours is a relatively small project, your range might be $30,000 to $50,000 to be

Duplicating this page is illegal. Do not copy this material without written permission from the publisher.

competitive. Remember, you want your proposal to seem attractive and cost-effective so that the granting agency feels that they are getting a lot of good work for their funding.

2. Draw up a comprehensive budget narrative, going back and forth between the budget and the work plan. It is a good idea to delve into these two sections at the same time.

3. Analyze the grand total, which will almost always be higher than it should be, and fine-tune your budget and work plan as needed.

Where Can Funds Be Obtained?

There are a variety of potential funding sources for Project Northland. First, be sure you have adequately pursued any possibilities available through your school, your school district, or the organization implementing the program. Next, look one or two levels beyond your organization to umbrella organizations, such as the following:

- city and county health department funds
- school-distributed funds that may be available for you to use for a program such as Project Northland—you can find out by asking participating schools
- federal Title I, Title IV, and Title V funds, where appropriate
- city block grants—some organizations have found eager sponsorship from local businesses
- parents, especially through the local PTA, PTO, or other parent organization

Once you have looked locally, consider outside funding sources. Government initiatives are the primary source of funding for programs of this type. Look beyond the school to funding that is available from the district or from federal funding sources, such as the U.S. Department of Education, especially through the Office of Safe and Drug-Free Schools (http://www.ed.gov/about /offices/list/osdfs/programs.html).

Duplicating this page is illegal. Do not copy this material without written permission from the publisher.

Other potential funders include the following:

- the U.S. Department of Justice, Office of Juvenile Justice and Delinquency Prevention (http://ojjdp.ncjrs.org)

- national parent organizations

- Web sites such as Scholastic's searchable database of funding information (http://www.scholastic.com/administrator/funding/fundingconnection/fundingopportunities)

Your Hazelden outreach coordinator can offer more ideas. Hazelden contact information is included on the CD-ROM.

 PROFESSIONAL HIGHLIGHT

CASE EXAMPLE 4

Supportive Coalition-Facilitated Strategic Resource Use

By implementing Project Northland, the regional office described on page 36 was able to build on relationships established with the existing volunteer-driven community coalition. This coalition had been providing substance abuse prevention for about five years and established partnerships with nearly twenty local school districts. Also, they had purchased two mobile Life Education Centers (LECs) for instructing elementary school students about the importance of healthy lifestyle choices. Project Northland offered the opportunity to extend the coalition's messages through junior high and high school.

Backed by a wealth of local needs data, the partnership obtained grant funds to help offset program costs and developed a strategy to use what slim financial resources were available from the communities. Schools that participate in the LEC programs have made a per-pupil payment toward the costs of these programs since their inception, drawn from their Safe and Drug-Free Schools Title IV formula grants. Also, funding is designated from the "governor's initiative" portion of their state's Safe and Drug-Free Schools and Communities Program to help sustain prevention efforts. This funding, supplemented with locally raised funds, has enabled the region to employ five full-time staff members dedicated to annually helping approximately fifty classroom teachers in twenty-four schools reach more than three thousand students and their families through Project Northland.

This regional office has used its strengths creatively and efficiently to achieve success, despite its large geographic size and poverty across much of the region. Local program evaluation data indicate that monthly and annual alcohol use is about 20 percent lower among Project Northland participants than their local counterparts, and 29 percent lower than their national peers.

Duplicating this page is illegal. Do not copy this material without written permission from the publisher.

PROFESSIONAL HIGHLIGHT

"Our results show significant positive change in kids' perception that alcohol is harmful and in their knowledge about alcohol."

SAFE AND DRUG-FREE SCHOOLS PROGRAM COORDINATOR (NORTH CAROLINA)

How Is Project Northland's Evidence Base an Asset?

When a granting agency considers which projects to fund, it has to decide between many worthy applicants. The agency wants to know that its funding will be well spent. The grantor will therefore try to choose the organization that performs meaningful work that can actually be achieved with the allotted time and resources.

Project Northland is an evidence-based program listed on the Substance Abuse and Mental Health Services Administration (SAMHSA) National Registry of Evidence-based Programs and Practices (NREPP). That means it is based on research and proven to yield positive results in a wide variety of communities.

NREPP is a searchable database of effective programs designed to prevent and treat mental health and substance use disorders. Many government grants require that funded programs be listed in this registry. Project Northland's listing on NREPP establishes it as a program worthy of funding consideration.

 PROGRAM TIP

Plan for Program Sustainability
PART 1

Think long term when you project costs and search for funding:

• Budget for, and request, the funding needed for several years of program implementation, allowing for more than one full curriculum cycle.

• Tap into prevention and community safety money that may be available at the county level and beyond.

• Identify local organizations that may help fund consumables, such as photocopies and *Slick Tracy* comic books. Auto insurance companies, civic organizations, or local businesses may contribute to the prevention of underage alcohol use and drunk driving.

• Keep good records of all funding inquiries and applications; funders that reject an application now may accept one later for a program that is further developed.

• Keep good records of your expenses to help with budgeting in the future.

• Build and maintain positive relationships with funders to help pave the way for ongoing Project Northland funds for your community.

Duplicating this page is illegal. Do not copy this material without written permission from the publisher.

What Is the Best Way to Write a Grant Proposal?

There is no one right way to write a grant, but there is sufficient standardization of grant components and grantor requirements to make the process fairly uniform. The advantage of this uniformity is that each time you write a grant, you will be able to use some familiar templates and procedures, and you will be able to improve your grant-writing skills.

Here are some common steps in the grant-writing process:

1. **Analyze need**

    a. Gather knowledge about the problem of teen alcohol use. A wealth of information and resources is provided in this manual and on the CD-ROM to help you get started.

    b. Gather information about local conditions that demonstrate specific local needs in your area. Review data gathered by your schools, news media, law enforcement, and community groups regarding attendance rates, alcohol-related traffic accidents or mortality, and more. What local statistics or sadly familiar tragedy can help you demonstrate the need for effective alcohol-use prevention? Think about why you want to implement Project Northland. Your reasons— or those of your school or organization—are likely to be compelling.

 PROGRAM TIP

Free Resource May Help with Needs Analysis

FACE is a national nonprofit organization that supports sensible alcohol policies and offers a document called the Community Alcohol Personality Survey. This document is intended to help you "learn how to establish the size and shape of alcohol problems in your community and where to focus your efforts for the most impact." You may find this resource particularly helpful while working on your needs assessment. FACE offers other resources, too. Information about FACE and its Web site is in Resources and Links by Topic on the CD-ROM.

Duplicating this page is illegal. Do not copy this material without written permission from the publisher.

c. Write a needs assessment: a qualitative and quantitative description of the specific problems and conditions that Project Northland will address in your area. You may consult the Project Northland Funding Toolkit on your CD-ROM for ideas.

d. Gather demographic information about your community and historical information about approaches already introduced to address the problem.

2. **Plan**

a. Get together with others to share your findings and ideas. Connect with both school staff—administrators, teachers, and others—and community members, parents and guardians, business owners, law enforcement, and others. Gather information, ideas, and support to inform and strengthen your plans.

b. Prepare a detailed budget and work plan, including a timeline.

c. Identify the most appropriate funding sources for your plans.

d. Contact the funders for current guidelines and proposal submission dates. Also, find out when funding awards are delivered. You won't want to plan a project starting in October if funds first become available in May.

e. Get back together with others who can help develop your plans. Share your progress and continue to gather their input and support as you move ahead.

3. **Write**

a. Consult the Project Northland Funding Toolkit and fact sheets on the CD-ROM. The funding toolkit provides many of the resources you will need to develop a grant application. Included you will find these documents:

• Guide to Successful Grant Writing

 Duplicating this page is illegal. Do not copy this material without written permission from the publisher.

- Grant Application Template
- Sample Letter Requesting a Letter of Commitment
- Sample Letter of Commitment

b. Follow all guidelines provided by the grant-sponsoring agency. Use any checklists provided by the agency and follow these precisely. In grant competitions with many applicants, avoid procedural errors that could disqualify your proposal.

c. Supplement your needs assessment with additional research as needed.

d. Review other strong grant proposals as models.

e. Complete each section of the grant proposal according to its purpose. Check to be sure, for example, that

- the "problem" section explains the significant risks to health, safety, and community posed by underage drinking
- the "work plan" includes a detailed timeline
- you clearly state your goals and objectives
- the "evaluation" section includes an evaluation plan

f. Make sure you include all of the required items. For instance, some funders require a logic model. Some require a detailed evaluation plan. Provide everything requested.

4. Continue applying

a. Once you have sent one grant proposal, do not rely on its approval. Begin another as soon as possible.

b. Keep talking with interested community members and others who have a stake in the success of your program.

c. Be sure to include local business leaders in your conversations.

Duplicating this page is illegal. Do not copy this material without written permission from the publisher.

Construct a Compelling Grant Proposal

Here are some key aspects of compelling grant applications:

- **Significance:** It is important to establish that there is a significant problem or need. When writing your Project Northland grant proposal, you must show the significance of underage alcohol use. Facts in your funding toolkit, in this manual, online, and from your community needs analysis will all help you show significance.

- **Inherency:** Show that the problem is inherent to the status quo; it can't simply be cleared up some other way, and it will not go away by itself. Show that Project Northland is the best solution available. When writing your Project Northland grant proposal, include facts indicating that other programs do not work as well, that addressing the issue among middle school students is essential, and that failing to do so will result in undesired consequences. Again, you can draw on many resources to prove these points.

- **Plan:** The grant writer needs to lay out a clear plan that directly links the need to desired results. In this case, you have selected a strong, proven curriculum. You just have to show that you have a clear plan for how to implement the curriculum. Describe the who, what, where, and when of using Project Northland.

- **Solvency:** Provide indicators that your plan will solve the problem in a significant way. For your Project Northland grant proposal, draw upon the Project Northland research papers and fact sheets on the CD-ROM and past results of others who have used the curriculum to show that your plan is likely to be an effective way to reduce alcohol use, delay the age at which students drink, and improve their understanding of safe alternative behaviors.

The trick to effective grant writing is to demonstrate the significance and inherency of underage drinking in the community, and

Duplicating this page is illegal. Do not copy this material without written permission from the publisher.

to have a clear plan that directly links this problem to desired improvements that can be expected to result in a solution that will be significant, long lasting, and sustainable.

What Are Some More Tricks of the Grant-Writing Trade?

1. **Allow plenty of time.** Creating a strong, complete grant application may take several months, especially if this is your first one.

2. **Be comprehensive.** Think through all details now to avoid surprises later.

3. **Be current.** For example, check allowable charges for travel or mileage reimbursement, because these change over time.

4. **Use Microsoft Excel** or another spreadsheet program, if possible, to create a detailed budget.

5. Double-, triple-, and quadruple-**check everything!**

6. **Follow the sequence and format shown in the grantor's guidelines.** Show that you are not sending a generic proposal—even if in some ways you are—but one tailored for the agency and representing a project that is just the sort of thing that that agency funds.

7. In the salary section of your budget narrative, if you have one, **show the per-hour pay of each staff person and the number of hours** that he or she is spending on Project Northland. (You may group staff who are spending the same number of hours on the project and are paid the same amount per hour.) Alternatively, you can show the cost per academic year for each person, the fraction of full time that person is giving to Project Northland, and the total cost for the person's time. When you show these amounts, use the actual wages for people who you know will be on staff (accounting for any expected pay increases, since grants usually take effect in the year subsequent to the one in which applications are made). If you do not know exactly who will fill all the positions, try to budget

PROFESSIONAL HIGHLIGHT

"Scale scores for eighth graders at the end of Project Northland (8.35) were better than for the comparison group (10.05), indicating better refusal skills in the Project Northland group."

WILDER RESEARCH (MINNESOTA)

Duplicating this page is illegal. Do not copy this material without written permission from the publisher.

slightly on the high side. If you only know average wages for certain positions, you can usually use them fairly safely.

Include the cost of benefits for those employees who are eligible. Consultants and many hourly or part-time workers do not receive benefits. Also, you may want to list fees for consultants—such as trainers and evaluators—in another section of a grant proposal, separate from employees with set salaries and benefits. Remember to include your own salary, even if it is an in-kind donation.

8. When writing the budget narrative—the detailed part of a proposal budget—**write out all calculations** with words and numbers. For example, write out estimated photocopying expenses like this:

   200 copies x $.08/copy x 2 semesters = $32.

9. Often, a match is required, and it is almost always desired. *Matches* or *matching funds* are funds that your group provides to cover a portion of program expenses. In other words, grantors do not always want to pay for everything. They want to see that your organization has an investment in your project— literally as well as in spirit.

   If your organization does not seem to have funds to contribute, don't despair. Usually, matching funds may be in-kind payments. *In-kind* means that your organization does not actually write a check. Instead, it contributes the use of its resources, such as staff time, phone use, office space, classrooms, meeting space, and computers.

   Every project requires resources to which your entity already has access. People have to meet, and schools have meeting space. Staff may have time to do some work on the project within the hours for which they are already paid. For example, do you have an office assistant who has two hours available weekly for administrative grant work? Do you have a computer technician on call? Do you have a gymnasium or cafeteria where an *Amazing Alternatives* event can be held? Copy machines, telephones, computers, and other tools are all valuable assets.

Duplicating this page is illegal. Do not copy this material without written permission from the publisher.

Use these resources. Plan them into your grant because you will need them. Estimate their market value. For example, if your grant involves three *Amazing Alternatives* events, you probably have access to space in which the event can be held. Similar space might rent for $300 per evening, so you can provide a $300 in-kind match per event. That's a total of $900 for three events! (Then you can use donated refreshments and publicity to create the events, or use grant funds to pay for these.)

10. Here is something to keep in mind for an in-kind match: If you are giving office space to staff to use for the project, **you can estimate a total of up to 25 percent of dedicated employees' salaries to office setup.** That's a nice amount of match that costs nothing but a little space, an existing computer and/or desk, and some setup time.

11. When you think your budget is finished, **run it by two administrators with experience in budgeting and, if possible, an accountant** who provides service to your school district or agency. See if the budget looks reasonable and comprehensive to them. If not, make sensible adjustments. Be sure to check all your numbers again and to make sure that the budget narrative and budget summary match.

How Can I Ensure That My Proposal Will Be Considered?

It cannot be stressed enough that it is vital to meet the terms of the grant:

- Be sure that the grant plan is written with its focus on accomplishing a goal the grantor intends to support.

- Be sure that each section of the proposal follows the grant's guidelines in terms of its content, organization, length, format, and deadline.

- Be sure that you send the number of copies requested (sometimes, even the number of originals and single- or double-sided copying is specified) with proper signatures.

PROFESSIONAL HIGHLIGHT

"Feedback on the first grant cycle was super-positive."

COMMUNITY COALITION COORDINATOR (MINNESOTA)

Duplicating this page is illegal. Do not copy this material without written permission from the publisher.

• Be on time. If possible, leave yourself an extra day or two, just in case the proposal or printing take longer than you want. Send proposals by FedEx or overnight mail, send them electronically, or hand-deliver them in person or by courier, but *do not be even one minute late*. A true story tells of an applicant who located the grantor's office eight minutes after the application period had closed and had his grant proposal refused for consideration. If possible, make sure that the proposal arrives one or more days before the deadline date. Check with the courier or use shipping records (or deliver it yourself and note the name of the person accepting it) to document your proposal's arrival at the right place and on time.

What Tips Do You Have for Keeping Grantors Happy— and Funding Coming In?

No one—parent, friend, or funder—likes someone they have helped out to take the money and run. They want to know and see how their contributions are helping people; they want to have an ongoing relationship with the recipient of the funds; they want the recipient to adhere to the terms of their agreement; and they feel good when the recipient gives them credit for making good work possible.

Grantors make an investment when they make an award to a program. They stake their resources and reputation on that investment. In return for the resources that make programming possible, granting agencies want to receive certain things:

• timely, respectful communication

• adherence to all guidelines

• thorough evaluations, showing inputs and outcomes clearly

• appreciation, in the form of letters and e-mails from you, students, parents and guardians, and/or other community members

• good publicity, like credit in your flyers and news releases

Duplicating this page is illegal. Do not copy this material without written permission from the publisher.

You can keep grantors happy by providing these services and benefits. Keeping grantors happy is absolutely crucial to procuring future funding, both from that agency and from others.

What Other Resources Will I Find Useful in Securing Funding?

There are many books and Web-based resources that you may find helpful in grant writing. You will find an excellent, specifically tailored resource if you refer to the detailed Project Northland Funding Toolkit on the CD-ROM that accompanies this manual. Useful Web sites are also referenced on the CD-ROM.

Summary

You start out with several advantages when seeking funds for Project Northland:

- There is a strong need for effective alcohol-use prevention in nearly every community.

- Project Northland is research based, evidence based, rigorously tested, and proven effective.

- Many districts and states set aside funding for prevention programs.

- This guide and many free online resources can help make your quest for funding surer and easier.

There are grant-sponsoring organizations and agencies available to help. Also, your school district or state may have some funding set aside for prevention. Businesses and private philanthropic organizations may contribute support.

·　·　·

Duplicating this page is illegal. Do not copy this material without written permission from the publisher.

Implementing Project Northland

This chapter provides tips for establishing relationships at schools and in the community, building excitement around Project Northland, training staff, and launching the program at your site.

▶▶ *What You Will Learn in Chapter 5:*

• What are the main steps in Project Northland implementation?

• How are staff trained to deliver Project Northland?

• What is a Community Launch Party?

What Are the Main Steps in Project Northland Implementation?

Although it is ideal to establish a base of community support before introducing the curricula, circumstances often dictate that curriculum implementation serves as a catalyst for community involvement. The diagram on the next page shows key steps to take when implementing Project Northland. The steps outlined are roughly sequential. Some overlap. Program evaluation and sustainability efforts continually inform and renew implementation.

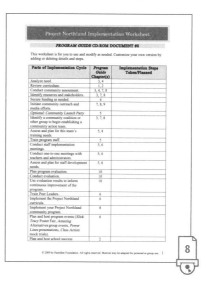

There is a worksheet version of these steps on the CD-ROM. You can copy, customize, and print the CD-ROM worksheet as needed.

Duplicating this page is illegal. Do not copy this material without written permission from the publisher.   59

Project Northland Implementation Cycle

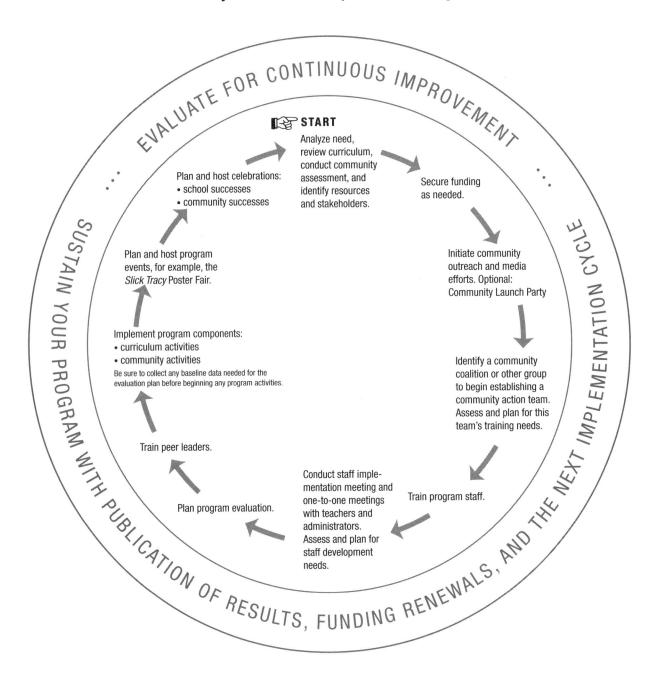

EVALUATE FOR CONTINUOUS IMPROVEMENT

SUSTAIN YOUR PROGRAM WITH PUBLICATION OF RESULTS, FUNDING RENEWALS, AND THE NEXT IMPLEMENTATION CYCLE

☞ **START**
Analyze need, review curriculum, conduct community assessment, and identify resources and stakeholders.

Secure funding as needed.

Initiate community outreach and media efforts. Optional: Community Launch Party

Identify a community coalition or other group to begin establishing a community action team. Assess and plan for this team's training needs.

Train program staff.

Conduct staff implementation meeting and one-to-one meetings with teachers and administrators. Assess and plan for staff development needs.

Plan program evaluation.

Train peer leaders.

Implement program components:
• curriculum activities
• community activities
Be sure to collect any baseline data needed for the evaluation plan before beginning any program activities.

Plan and host program events, for example, the *Slick Tracy* Poster Fair.

Plan and host celebrations:
• school successes
• community successes

Duplicating this page is illegal. Do not copy this material without written permission from the publisher.

What Is the Best Way to Roll Out the Project Northland Curricula?

Many communities choose to introduce Project Northland incrementally, while others decide to initiate all grades simultaneously. Some may choose to introduce *Class Action,* the high school component, after first establishing the middle grades. Your trainer can recommend the best plan for how to roll out Project Northland with your community. The best approach depends on several things:

▧ **What is the scope of your implementation? Schoolwide? Districtwide? Other?**

The larger your implementation, the less individual time you will have for each classroom or even each school. On the other hand, with wider implementation, you may have proportionately more funding, a bigger volunteer base, and more community resources.

▧ **What is your budget?**

The availability of funds will influence how much in-class support, supervision, and modeling you can offer to teachers. This manual offers many choices. Select the ones that fit with your needs and resources.

▧ **What is the character of your community?**

You may also make choices that fit with your community's structures, institutions, and size, as well as choices that are influenced by whether it is rural, suburban, or urban and by other characteristics explored in chapter 3.

Options for Getting Started

INCREMENTAL MIDDLE SCHOOL PHASE-IN

With a three-phase model, a coordinator provides scaffolding to support teachers' mastery of the curriculum. During phase 1, the coordinator or another demonstration teacher delivers *Slick Tracy* while the classroom teachers observe. In phase 2, the coordinator

PROFESSIONAL HIGHLIGHT

"In Portland, 508 Class Action *students were asked about the program . . . Seventy-one percent rated* Class Action *as 'excellent' or 'good,' and 61 percent recommended using* Class Action *with next year's students."*

PACIFIC RESEARCH AND EVALUATION (OREGON)

Duplicating this page is illegal. Do not copy this material without written permission from the publisher.

and classroom teachers collaborate, often as a tag team, to carry out Peer Leader training, classroom delivery, and student support. In phase 3, the coordinator has a minimal role, supporting the classroom teacher. Typically, this process occurs over three consecutive school years, with *Amazing Alternatives* and *Power Lines* introduced in like manner while *Slick Tracy* is in phases 2 and 3, respectively.

Advantages to this approach include the following:

1. All Project Northland alumni will have experienced the entire curriculum.

2. Training may be delivered in smaller parcels as needed; in areas with high teacher mobility, this may improve sustainability.

3. The initial cost of materials will be lower.

4. The community has more time to learn about Project Northland and learn alongside implementers.

5. Thorough training that provides focused resources and full support to each grade level consecutively may yield stronger outcomes and community impact.

ALL-GRADE MIDDLE SCHOOL IMPLEMENTATION

Alternatively, communities may choose to begin implementing in grades six, seven, and eight simultaneously. Substantial resources are required to accomplish this with adequate support.

Advantages to this approach include the following:

1. No students in targeted grades are left unprotected by the prevention program.

2. Most of the students acquire background skills and information that they can build upon in subsequent years.

3. Training and community events may be more cost and time effective.

4. The community experiences the program as a whole from the start.

Duplicating this page is illegal. Do not copy this material without written permission from the publisher.

5. Having the program reach more students, parents, and community members right away may yield earlier outcomes and community impact.

6. Sustainability may be greater with so many people informed, trained, and initiated.

 PROGRAM TIP

It is recommended that schools implementing all grades at once give their seventh graders both *Slick Tracy* early in the school year and *Amazing Alternatives* later the same year.

HIGH SCHOOL IMPLEMENTATION

Some schools have found it helpful to introduce *Class Action* by first taking the whole class through the process of preparing one case together. This case is used as a model for teaching students about program expectations, legal terminology, and the process of building a case before having them work more independently on the other cases in small cooperative groups.

How Are Staff Trained to Deliver Project Northland?

What Are the Goals of Training?

The most important goal of Project Northland training is to ensure program fidelity. Training also helps staff learn the curriculum and helps communities address alcohol prevention effectively. Skilled trainers provide a strong foundation for implementing with fidelity. Training presents an opportunity to learn from the experiences of others who have implemented Project Northland many times.

Training is an opportunity for participants to

• discuss comprehensive prevention in relation to Project Northland

• learn about Project Northland

Duplicating this page is illegal. Do not copy this material without written permission from the publisher.

- acquire effective strategies to prevent and reduce teen use of alcohol, cigarettes, and other drugs
- interact with other professionals and educators committed to youth health and safety
- shift the community toward no-use norms for underage drinking

Training brings together the key staff with whom you will work. It helps build camaraderie and a sense of mission. Use some of this time to connect with teachers and schedule individual follow-up meetings.

What Takes Place at Training Sessions?

A Project Northland training opens with an introduction similar to what one might present at a Community Launch Party. The trainer uses this introduction to make participants keenly aware of the need for effective alcohol-use prevention with the targeted age group.

You will spend most of the day on the nuts and bolts of the program, the experiential pieces that teachers will share with their classes. A typical training includes a thorough overview of the program components and session-by-session preparation with opportunities to experience key activities such as role playing and brainstorming. Participants preview both printed and audio materials and work together in small groups. Time is allotted for questions and discussion.

During the program, people may become more sensitized to alcohol-related issues. Consider inviting an administrator to explain referral procedures for connecting students and families with support services. Students may bring concerns about under-age drinking or other alcohol-related issues to the attention of their teachers, so it is a good idea to be prepared with knowledge about community resources and how to access them.

Trainings vary in length from one to several days. A link to more information is on the CD-ROM.

Duplicating this page is illegal. Do not copy this material without written permission from the publisher.

What Is the Coordinator's Role in Project Northland Training?

The program coordinator is the host, the organizer, and the contact person for Project Northland trainings. The CD-ROM provides a Project Northland Training Worksheet to help you get ready.

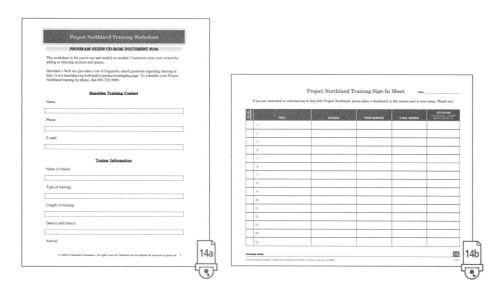

Contact Hazelden to connect with a representative who will set up your training. Preparation includes publicity, invitations, arranging a space, food, and any decorations. You may help arrange your trainer's stay and provide transportation to and from the airport, if needed.

On training days, you will want to arrive early to make sure everything is ready and to welcome guests as they arrive. It is also a good idea to plan on staying late so you can answer questions, clean up, and jot a few notes for planning. To build rapport and learn more, you might also want to make informal dinner plans with your trainer.

Throughout the day, you will learn alongside your staff. You may be called upon to assist the trainer as needed or communicate with people in charge of the space if anything is not working or needs to be adjusted. At the end of the training, thank the trainer and all who attended. Schedule a staff implementation meeting

Duplicating this page is illegal. Do not copy this material without written permission from the publisher.

65

to occur within the next two weeks. Also schedule individual meetings with the teachers.

The sections that follow give more details about how to prepare for this training.

How Do I Schedule Training?

It is best to schedule your training at least sixty days in advance. To schedule a Project Northland training, contact Hazelden using the information on your CD-ROM. Web site, e-mail, and phone contacts are provided. Depending on your school's needs, training will probably take one or two days.

What Is the Best Way to Prepare for Training?

First, reserve a space. You will want a space that can accommodate up to thirty people, has audiovisual resources, and will be easy for participants to get to on the training days. Make sure the space either allows catering or has access to nearby food venues. Choose a space where people will feel comfortable and be able to concentrate on learning.

Next, invite and inform participants. Clarify in advance whether Project Northland training is optional or required for your teachers. (It should be required.) Also clarify whether or not participants will be compensated for their time and, if so, how. Connect with your trainer by phone or e-mail.

What Should Be Considered When Preparing the Guest List and Invitations?

It is essential to train all the teachers who will deliver Project Northland curricula to your students. Also, you will want to invite administrators, volunteers, community members, and others who will be involved with Project Northland implementation.

Establish clear expectations with the participants. They may not be knowledgeable about the importance of underage alcohol-use prevention, so be sure to explain what Project Northland is and why it is important. You may want to attach one or two fact sheets from the CD-ROM to your invitations.

✏ PROFESSIONAL HIGHLIGHT

"Our teachers can get 60 of the 120 in-service points they need in order to renew their license every five years by doing Project Northland surveys and paperwork on themselves and their students. This incentive helps get people on board."

CHEMICAL HEALTH DIVISION PLANNER, STATE DEPARTMENT OF HUMAN SERVICES (MINNESOTA)

Duplicating this page is illegal. Do not copy this material without written permission from the publisher.

Let participants know that they should bring their calendars to schedule a staff implementation meeting for follow-up, as well as for individual consultations. Keep track of RSVPs and send reminders a few days before the training.

What Materials Are Needed?

Consult with your Hazelden contact about the specific materials your trainer needs, such as audiovisual equipment. The trainer may request that you photocopy the agenda he or she has prepared for your group. You may also want to prepare the following items to accompany the training materials your trainer will distribute:

- your contact information

- one or more fact sheets with relevant facts about youth and alcohol

- information about lunch plans or options

- mileage form or parking reimbursement form (if paying participants' travel expenses)

- a checklist of what you need from each participant by the end of the day, such as completed evaluation form, completed reimbursement form, scheduled appointment with you, and so on

Make sure the curriculum materials themselves have been delivered, with enough copies so you will be able to give one to each participant.

You may also want to have these items on hand:

- posters from Hazelden

- student work samples from other local implementers

- highlighters, pencils, sticky notes, and candy for each table

- a large presentation-size sticky pad and markers on an easel

- white board and white-board markers

Duplicating this page is illegal. Do not copy this material without written permission from the publisher.

What Refreshments Are Appropriate?

It is gracious and inviting to offer food and beverages. Make food choices as festive, fresh, healthy, and high quality as possible. What to offer depends on both your resources and your training schedule. If your budget is tight, you may want to serve only hot coffee, tea, and chilled water.

What Should the Training Room Look Like When People Arrive?

The room should be inviting. Ask your trainer about his or her preferences for the seating arrangements and audiovisual equipment.

You will want to greet participants when they arrive, have them sign in, and give each one a name tag and a packet. Inside the training room, the space should be fully prepared with all necessary training materials, examples of end projects (such as student posters), and Project Northland posters. The trainer will do this preparation with you or for you.

What Follow-Up Should I Do After Training?

The kind of follow-up to do will depend on your teachers' needs. The recommended approach is to both reconvene all teaching staff to clarify implementation plans and meet individually with teachers to learn about any questions or concerns they may have and any help they may need. Both types of follow-up should occur before implementation begins, ideally within two weeks following the training.

A staff implementation meeting provides you with another opportunity to build your relationships with the teaching staff, and it provides teachers with an opportunity to ask questions. It is a good time for you to clarify expectations, such as

- how materials will be distributed
- your role and what support you offer to teachers
- plans for program evaluation and collection of baseline data
- how many times you need to observe in each classroom

Duplicating this page is illegal. Do not copy this material without written permission from the publisher.

• the purpose of individual consultations

• anticipated frequency of communications

Individual consultations are both for reviewing the classroom checklist (on the CD-ROM) and for offering support. Some teachers will want both technical and teaching support, some will want only technical support (materials, photocopying, and so on), and others will want very little support at all. Some teachers will want you to visit the class as often as possible. Others might find such visits intrusive. Find out what type of support each individual wants and needs, as well as his or her preferred mode of communication. Chapter 6 offers more ideas about how to establish a supportive professional rapport at these initial meetings and offer ongoing support. Be sure to meet with each teacher in his or her classroom so you can see the layout and get a sense of the implementation space.

 PROGRAM TIP

Plan for Program Sustainability
PART 2

Your good records and good manners will prove invaluable later:

• Keep track of materials.

• Take notes on what you learn.

• Record all donors and donations.

• Thank everyone graciously and publicly for their involvement, donations, and support.

• Continue to inform people about underage drinking issues, Project Northland, and how to get involved.

• Establish teacher buy-in and positive relationships with teachers.

Duplicating this page is illegal. Do not copy this material without written permission from the publisher.

What Is a Community Launch Party?

There are times when it is both desirable and feasible to deliver Project Northland training to people from many sectors of the community at once, but most of the time this simply does not happen. Another way to inform people about Project Northland and create excitement around the program is to host a Community Launch Party. If you choose to do this, you may want to use the planning worksheet on the CD-ROM.

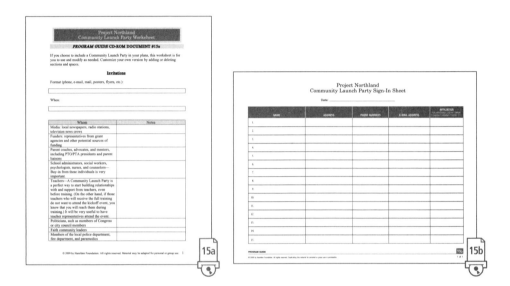

A kickoff event like this serves several functions:

■ **It casts a wide net for inclusion.** People who cannot attend daytime trainings may still attend the launch party to gain key information and become involved. Those who may not need to deliver the curriculum—safety officers, parents and guardians, school and county administrators, health care providers, and media—can be included in this way.

■ **It takes the program beyond school walls into the community.** Since parent and community involvement are two components of successful implementation, this bridge building is important.

■ **It builds excitement about Project Northland.**

Duplicating this page is illegal. Do not copy this material without written permission from the publisher.

■ **It establishes positive expectations for the program:**

— Project Northland is a comprehensive, evidence-based, and research-based prevention program that has been proven effective. In fact, the community is getting to take part in the best alcohol-use prevention program available!

— Project Northland does not just involve the school; it involves everyone.

— Project Northland is fun, engaging, and relevant.

Who May Be Invited to a Community Launch Party?

Invite all the key people you hope to involve in your program. Consider the following:

1. School administrators, social workers, psychologists, nurses, and/or counselors

2. Teachers—a Community Launch Party is a nice, informal way to begin building relationships with teachers before training. Since training is required for teachers, you may choose to emphasize that their attendance at this party is optional, but it is helpful to have a few teacher representatives present.

3. Parents, coaches, advocates, and mentors, including PTO/PTA presidents, parent liaisons, and so on

4. Reporters from local newspapers, radio stations, and television stations

5. People from granting organizations and others who may offer funding

6. Community leaders:

   • government officials, such as local congressional representatives or city council members

   • public health personnel

   • law enforcement personnel and first responders

   • faith community leaders

   • doctors and emergency room staff

Duplicating this page is illegal. Do not copy this material without written permission from the publisher.

- business leaders
- liquor store owners, bar owners, and Responsible Beverage Service (RBS) trainers
- representatives from youth-serving organizations
- youth leaders and other interested youth
- county court personnel, judges, and bar association members
- substance abuse counselors and treatment providers
- representatives from advocacy groups such as Partnership for a Drug-Free America, SADD, MADD, and Leadership to Keep Children Alcohol Free (this last group is a coalition of governors' spouses—maybe yours is a member and will come to support your Project Northland program)

Surely, you will not want to invite all of these people, but you will want to identify which would best support your Project Northland program and include them on your guest list. Assemble a group that is inclusive but manageable and that will help you achieve your goals.

What Happens at a Community Launch Party?
When planning the event, keep in mind these goals:
- informing the public
- promoting Project Northland
- including representation from the entire community
- gaining the support and involvement of sponsors, volunteers, media, and others
- celebrating the community's launch of Project Northland

Consider how you want to convey information through your event. Plan for a presentation area that can be seen clearly by everyone, a screen, a microphone, and at least one information table. You might also display posters and student work from other sites.

Duplicating this page is illegal. Do not copy this material without written permission from the publisher.

To convey a feeling of celebration, you might use colored construction paper for simple decorating on tables. If available, student artwork, plants and flowers, or balloons and confetti may be used to create a festive environment. Serve delicious, plentiful, and healthy refreshments.

Designate a table near the entrance where guests will sign in and receive name tags and, perhaps, a small gift such as candy, a flower, or coupons from local businesses. Provide handouts to help participants learn more about Project Northland and underage drinking issues.

Volunteers, if available, may help you greet guests as they arrive. Greeters can help make sure that everyone provides contact information when they sign in, and they can encourage others to sign up as volunteers. Use the template on your CD-ROM to prepare sign-up sheets for volunteers and sponsors willing to donate the following:

- **time:** to support a class, grade level, or school; as a *Slick Tracy* Poster Fair judge; as a resource person students may contact for interviews during their *Power Lines* research; to make copies; to help train or teach

- **goods:** refreshments for a Poster Fair or an *Amazing Alternatives* event night; incentive prizes for program participation

- **services:** posting rights in a local storefront; free or discounted photocopying; announcement space in a local publication; and so on

If a Project Northland trainer is available—perhaps arriving the day before training—this can enhance the presentation. If a trainer is not available, you will want to plan your own presentation to accurately convey the answers to these questions:

- What is Project Northland?

- Why is alcohol-use prevention important, especially in middle school and high school?

Duplicating this page is illegal. Do not copy this material without written permission from the publisher.

73

- Why use Project Northland?

- What opportunities are there for people to get involved and offer support?

Present for about twenty minutes or less. You will want to show the first part of the Project Northland DVD during this time. Remember to leave additional time at the end for questions and discussion. Help attendees to learn about the program and gain enthusiasm through your presentation.

Your presentation will model how to talk about underage alcohol use and Project Northland. Your warmth and engagement will model appropriate attitudes and enthusiasm for teachers and learners. Your conviction regarding the importance of prevention and positive program outcomes will also set an example.

Make the evening worth everyone's time. For fun, maybe a local celebrity could open the presentation with a statement of support, or a local ensemble could perform. Each person should gain information about Project Northland and a sense of involvement, a feeling that they have a stake in the program, and a desire to participate in some way.

Be sure to thank everyone for coming!

Summary

Thoughtful planning and professional training will pave the way for implementing the Project Northland curricula with fidelity and achieving strong outcomes. A Community Launch Party can create excitement and build your base of supporters. The next chapter offers suggestions for supporting teachers and learners during implementation.

PROFESSIONAL HIGHLIGHT

"Over 500 parents and students participated in this year's Project Northland Kick-Off on a fall evening in Randolph. Participants gathered information from 25 booths set up by community organizations including Boy Scouts, Red Cross, Public Health, and others. At the Public Health booth, participants received information about Project Northland's best practices."

E-NEWS FROM PUBLIC HEALTH, DECEMBER 2008, HTTP://WWW.DAKOTACOUNTY.US

* * *

Duplicating this page is illegal. Do not copy this material without written permission from the publisher.

CHAPTER 6

Supporting Teachers and Learners

Just as training before implementation is important, it is equally important to provide ongoing support during implementation. This chapter offers many ideas. Choose the ideas that best fit the needs of your program.

▶▶ *What You Will Learn in Chapter 6:*

- What essential support is most needed?
- How to conduct Peer Leader training
- What tips do Project Northland's most expert implementers recommend?

What Support Is Essential?

Teachers are busy professionals. Most simply do not have time for tasks like coordinating special events, community organizing, and program evaluation. An administrator, program coordinator, or task force needs to support these pieces of Project Northland implementation. Teachers may also need support in learning to implement the curriculum with students.

Establish a Supportive Professional Rapport with Teachers

Within two weeks after training, and before implementation, you will want to meet with each teacher individually. Teachers need to understand clearly what is expected from them. Clarifying your expectations may involve a process of negotiation with some teachers. It is most important to have up-front and open communication in the way that best suits each teacher's needs and style of communication. Find out how each teacher likes to be contacted—by phone, e-mail, or classroom visit—and if there are particular days or times of day when he or she is more readily available to meet.

At this first one-to-one meeting, it is a good idea to provide a menu of resources and support you can offer. Encourage each teacher to indicate what type of support he or she prefers and to schedule additional consultation and

Duplicating this page is illegal. Do not copy this material without written permission from the publisher.

classroom visits. Review the classroom checklist (which is found on the CD-ROM) together. Set a truly supportive tone, one of encouragement and assistance rather than judgment.

Take Responsibility for Peer Leader Training

The program coordinator should take the lead in setting up Peer Leader training. This training is required for Project Northland's sixth- and seventh-grade curricula. Empower Peer Leaders with information, strategies, and experiences that nurture their leadership skills. Communicate with them periodically and celebrate their successes.

Provide Training, Support, and Encouragement to Teachers, Especially When Project Northland Is New to Them

Guest-teach in their classrooms to model program delivery, and reflect together on these sessions. Encourage and assist teachers who bring questions or challenges to your attention. You can be the one to research the answers. Call your trainer, collect ideas from other teachers or administrators, find the answers, and get back to the teacher in a timely manner.

Oversee Program Evaluation

Evaluation is very important. It will help you measure your success and make improvements as you move ahead. See chapter 10 for information about how to coordinate program evaluation.

How to Conduct Peer Leader Training

Peer leadership is an essential component of Project Northland. Research shows that teens are more receptive to social information received from respected peers than from adults. Before Peer Leader training, be sure that teachers send home the letters for parents and guardians that are provided in the *Amazing Alternatives* and *Slick Tracy* curricula, and prepare a Peer Leader Manual for each participant.

Instructions for Peer Leader training are outlined in the Teacher's Manuals for *Slick Tracy* and *Amazing Alternatives*,

Duplicating this page is illegal. Do not copy this material without written permission from the publisher.

and Peer Leader Manuals are on the CD-ROMs accompanying them. There are also planning resources on your CD-ROM. Peer Leader training is designed to prepare Peer Leaders for their new role working with groups of students in class. During the sessions, the students find out what is expected of them. They see the materials they will use and practice leading groups of their peers.

You will want to conduct separate Peer Leader trainings for *Slick Tracy* and *Amazing Alternatives.* Each training will take several hours, so it is desirable to train several classes—maybe even the whole grade level—at one time. The ideal group size for Peer Leader training is about twenty to twenty-five students. It is fine for students from several schools to be trained together if logistics allow for this. Peer Leader training must be completed before each curriculum's classroom sessions begin.

What Additional Support Is Helpful?

It is especially helpful for program coordinators or administrators to take responsibility for coordinating the *Slick Tracy* Poster Fair and other special events. Other ways you can offer support may be to do the following:

- Prepare curriculum materials such as photocopies and folders. See the CD-ROM for detailed session descriptions with preparation needed for each curriculum.

- Help teachers brainstorm to meet new challenges that arise.

- Bookmark useful Web sites and e-mail annotated lists with hyperlinks.

- Nurture relationships between teachers and others in the community.

Celebrate the progress of students and teachers, acknowledging them directly in person, through e-mails, and with thank-you notes. Publicize their accomplishments both within and beyond the school. Thank teachers publicly at special events and send

Duplicating this page is illegal. Do not copy this material without written permission from the publisher.

notes to their principals listing and praising their contributions to Project Northland.

💡 PROGRAM TIP

Wallet Card Resource for Students

A reproducible wallet card that lists emergency contacts for teens is included on the CD-ROM. Use of this card is optional. Distributing these to all Project Northland students can communicate a message that everyone needs help at times, and enable students to access services for their peers or themselves as needed. If you choose not to distribute these to the student body, there may be times when you want to discreetly offer it to specific students. Be sure to update your master wallet card as needed with current phone numbers and Web sites.

What Are Some Specific Ways to Support Each Curriculum?

Slick Tracy

The Poster Fair is the culminating event when sixth graders get to teach others about what they have learned. Organize the Poster Fair or supervise a volunteer group that will do this. Schedule one night when all the classes working on *Slick Tracy* can hold a joint Poster Fair.

💡 PROGRAM TIP

Schoolwide conference nights are busy times. Setting aside a separate night for the *Slick Tracy* Poster Fair is best and will result in a more focused, effective, and well-attended Poster Fair. However, you may want to schedule the Poster Fair on a night shortly before winter or spring conferences, so you can leave the posters up to be viewed by parents who will be at school during conference time.

Prepare invitations and flyers, and remind teachers to send these home at the appropriate times. Consider sending at least one set of invitations by mail. You might ask the art teacher to help students with their posters during art class. Invite community members and arrange for volunteers as needed. Arrange for refreshments. Prepare certificates for the students. Get someone

Duplicating this page is illegal. Do not copy this material without written permission from the publisher.

to take pictures. You might also want to make a printed program and recruit "judges," as described on the *Slick Tracy* CD-ROM.

Arrive early to be sure everything is set up properly. Stay late to help clean up. Be there to welcome people, talk very briefly about Project Northland as a whole, and congratulate and thank all participants. Spend time viewing posters and talking with parents and students. Afterward, you might display the posters out in the community.

Amazing Alternatives

Serve as an adviser to a student Alternatives group that meets after school to plan fun alcohol-free social events. Help the group develop their ideas. Schedule time when the students can host their events, and arrange for adult supervision. Help with invitations and posters. Support their plans for refreshments, decorations, and entertainment. Offer them materials about Project Northland and alcohol prevention to have on hand during the event. Arrange for volunteers to assist as needed. For more ideas, see Starting a Student Activity Group on your CD-ROM. The CD-ROM also provides kickoff planning ideas in Hosting an *Amazing Alternatives* Fun Night.

PROFESSIONAL HIGHLIGHT

"The seventh graders really seem to appreciate that Amazing Alternatives *is all about them."*

COMMUNITY COALITION COORDINATOR (MINNESOTA)

Duplicating this page is illegal. Do not copy this material without written permission from the publisher.

Power Lines

Create a list of community members willing to be interviewed by students doing community research projects to learn about underage drinking issues. You will want to obtain consent and contact information from each volunteer. Review the *Power Lines* projects to get a sense of the resources needed. Have the list ready when students begin their projects.

Create opportunities to share student projects beyond the classrooms. Ask local radio and television stations to air students' prevention messages, or post them online. You could host an event at school or organize a public display in the community.

Class Action

As a way to enhance your *Class Action* program, develop a list of contacts that includes lawyers, law students, and/or judges willing to help high school students prepare their *Class Action* cases. Also list those willing to act as "expert witnesses," such as pediatricians willing to share their knowledge of fetal alcohol syndrome. You will want to have consent and contact information for each volunteer.

You might want to share student presentations with the community by inviting guests to attend the mock trials in person. Also, you could record video of the mock trials to share them at a community gathering, online, or by sending copies to individuals. For example, a videotape (and routing schedule) could be sent home with students to circulate among the families in each class.

What Tips Do Project Northland's Most Expert Implementers Recommend?

Some of our most experienced implementers share these tips for going above and beyond to help your community realize its goals:

■ **Listen for what support is most wanted.** Teaching is endless and exhausting work. Help lighten teachers' loads in the ways they request.

■ PROFESSIONAL HIGHLIGHT

"I loved Power Lines. *We got very involved, went to city council meetings, and really got into it."*
ADMINISTRATOR (ALABAMA)

Duplicating this page is illegal. Do not copy this material without written permission from the publisher.

■ **Keep in touch.** Check in with the teachers from time to time, especially during the first week of Project Northland implementation and at the end of the program. Go above and beyond by sending articles, information, and notes of appreciation.

■ **Honor teachers' limited time and many responsibilities.** Take the responsibility off teachers for all parts of Project Northland that take place outside the classroom, including event planning, Peer Leader training, and community work. You don't need to do everything yourself, but do delegate and manage these items with other staff and volunteers.

■ **Demonstrate value.** Help teachers and administrators understand why this program is worth their time. When useful, explain how the program supports academic standards in many areas.

■ **Help prepare materials.** If your schedule and budget allow for it, photocopy all handouts, letters, and other Project Northland materials that teachers will need for implementation. This will help everyone be prepared to lead each session well, and it may help make you one of the most popular resource people at school!

■ **Help organize materials.** You might prepare file boxes for your teachers that contain all the supplies they need for Project Northland, from pencils to photocopies, so all a teacher has to do each week is open the week's folder and start teaching. At the end of the year, collect all the boxes. Replenish items as needed and prepare the boxes for the following year's teachers.

■ **Model and coach.** This helps build both competence and confidence. As much as possible, model sessions for teachers in their own classrooms. Afterward, reflect together on essential session components.

■ **Create meaningful experiences.** Add time in *Power Lines* for classes to go beyond their "community meeting" vote by having students research community projects that connect with the priorities they voted for. Adding this step makes the projects more meaningful.

Duplicating this page is illegal. Do not copy this material without written permission from the publisher.

- **Make time for reflection and sharing.** Reconvene teachers for a feedback session after they have experienced the curriculum. Try to secure funds to bring them together on paid time, with substitutes if needed, and provide refreshments. Offering this time as an opportunity to share experiences together will help foster professional development, continuous improvement, and a sustainable program.

Summary

By supporting teachers, you will help them develop ease and expertise with Project Northland. By making the program rewarding for teachers and fun for students, you will earn support from administrators, community members, and parents. In chapter 7, you will learn more about the role of families in Project Northland and gain strategies to help draw them in.

. . .

Duplicating this page is illegal. Do not copy this material without written permission from the publisher.

CHAPTER 7

Family Involvement

Family involvement is an essential component of Project Northland. It can be challenging to connect with parents and guardians, but it is important to involve as many families as possible. Project Northland offers many avenues for engaging diverse families, and this chapter offers a framework to help organize your family outreach efforts.

▶▶ *What You Will Learn in Chapter 7:*

- What does research indicate about family involvement?
- What family involvement opportunities does Project Northland provide?
- What types of outreach activities could draw more families into the program?

What Does Research Indicate about Family Involvement?

Numerous studies have documented that parents and other family members influence teens' decisions about whether or not to use alcohol. Teens who think that family members do not discourage their use of alcohol are more likely to drink than those who think otherwise. In general, it has been shown that if close friends or family members drink alcohol, an adolescent is likely to drink in a similar manner or under similar circumstances.

Family alcohol use, attitudes, and rules are not incidental to young people's alcohol use. In fact, they are vitally linked to it. *How Does Alcohol Affect the World of a Child?* is a pamphlet by Leadership to Keep Children Alcohol Free, a partnership of U.S. governors' spouses. It includes information about the importance of families, including the following:

- Parent drinking behaviors and parent attitudes that favor drinking are associated with underage alcohol use.

Duplicating this page is illegal. Do not copy this material without written permission from the publisher.

83

- Research studies show that children are less likely to drink when their parents are involved with them and when they and their parents report feeling close to each other.

- Adolescents drink less and have fewer alcohol-related problems when their parents discipline them consistently and set clear expectations.

- Older siblings' alcohol use can influence the alcohol use of younger siblings in the family, particularly for same-sex siblings.[1]

You may find this pamphlet to be a useful resource.

Project Northland and Parents as Partners in Prevention

Project Northland offers families a chance to keep their children safer and healthier. Project Northland also requires family involvement in order to succeed with its important work. In other words, parents and guardians have a stake in helping your program succeed, and you have a stake in keeping them involved. Understanding what you need from families and communicating what Project Northland offers to them will help you to connect effectively.

Families Need Project Northland

- to become better informed about why underage drinking is dangerous

- to gain awareness about issues and pressures in their children's lives

- to communicate more effectively with their children about alcohol and other tough subjects

- to make the community safer

- to educate their children about alcohol

- to empower their children to say no to alcohol and to make safer choices

- to prevent—or at least delay, reduce, and limit—their children's alcohol use

PROGRAM TIP

The Volunteer Sign-Up Sheets provided on the CD-ROM may be used to recruit parent volunteers. 16

Duplicating this page is illegal. Do not copy this material without written permission from the publisher.

- to reduce the likelihood of their children experimenting with other drugs
- to keep their loved ones safer and healthier

Project Northland Needs Families

- to help students complete homework assignments and plan fun alcohol-free events
- to attend special events
- to set up before, help during, and clean up after special events
- to attend student presentations
- to donate goods like food, tape, poster board, or flowers
- to donate services like photo processing and photocopying
- to post and distribute information, make phone calls, and seek sponsors
- to consent to having students interview them and consult them as resources
- to answer their own children's questions openly and accurately
- to spread the good word about your program
- to advocate for funding and classroom time
- to support and thank administrators and teachers for addressing this topic

RESEARCH FACT

Family Meals Reduce Risky Teen Behaviors
Researchers have found that teens who partake in regular meals with their families experience significant preventive benefits. It appears that the familiarity of the ritual itself is most important. With either one or two parents at meals, teens demonstrated less drinking, greater academic achievement, and fewer risky behaviors.[2]

What Family Involvement Opportunities Does Project Northland Provide?

Home Team Materials

Project Northland includes Home Team materials for parents and other significant adults to positively influence teens' alcohol-use decisions.

In *Slick Tracy,* specially designed activity booklets provide engaging shared activities to help open communication between young adolescents and their parents or guardians around alcohol

Duplicating this page is illegal. Do not copy this material without written permission from the publisher.

use. Project Northland's original research specifically targeted increasing parent-child communication and succeeded in increasing parent-child communication about the consequences of drinking. During *Slick Tracy*, students and their Home Team partners discuss alcohol issues in a way that is neither personal nor threatening, because they are discussing comic book characters rather than anyone they know. At the same time, families build and strengthen their ability to communicate about important topics. *Slick Tracy* Home Teams are assigned four of these comic books over four or more weeks. Weekly scorecards are included, and it is important for families to return these to school when they complete each comic book.

In *Amazing Alternatives* and *Power Lines,* reproducible Home Team materials further educate families and remind them to communicate clear expectations and a no-use message regarding underage alcohol use. Weekly Home Team materials are included with both programs.

Recommendations conveyed to parents through these materials include the following:

- Develop clear rules with appropriate consequences for alcohol use.

- Discuss and enforce rules.

- Monitor the activities of your children and know their friends.

- Recognize that you are a key role model for choices regarding alcohol use; your child is likely to behave as you do.

- Discuss mass media messages with your children.

- Provide fun alcohol-free activities.

- Reduce access to alcohol at home and in the community.

- Participate in school and community policy decisions.

The Home Team materials for both curricula also include activities to facilitate parent-teen interactions. *Amazing Alternatives* Home Team materials include mazes and games designed for teens to complete with their parents or guardians.

PROFESSIONAL HIGHLIGHT

"Seventy-two percent of eighth-grade Project Northland students say it is 'true' that their parents talk with them about problems drinking alcohol can cause young people, compared to 59 percent of the eighth-grade comparison group."

WILDER RESEARCH (MINNESOTA)

Duplicating this page is illegal. Do not copy this material without written permission from the publisher.

Power Lines Home Team series of eight send-home items includes four interactive games for teens and parents or guardians to play together. *Class Action* also includes Home Team materials.

Special Events and Celebrations

Project Northland also provides unique opportunities for parents to visit their child's school and participate in educational activities.

At the *Slick Tracy* Poster Fair, students present their own alcohol-related research projects to friends, family, and invited guests. The fair is a wonderful way to bring together the two worlds in which students have been working on this program: the family and the school. You can enhance this connection by

- recruiting parent and guardian volunteers to help plan and publicize the event
- scheduling the Poster Fair at a time when it is easy for parents and guardians to attend
- extending hospitality such as refreshments and door prizes

Be sure to use the letters and flyers included with the *Slick Tracy* curriculum to publicize this event effectively. If at all possible, send at least one of these items home by mail instead of with the students. At the event, seize the opportunity to thank and congratulate everyone for their participation.

Though *Amazing Alternatives* focuses more on peer interactions and social alternatives, there are plenty of opportunities for parents to get involved. Families with storefront businesses may allow students to advertise an *Amazing Alternatives* Fun Night or Student Activity Group meetings in their windows, as may homeowners. Families living in apartment buildings may be able to display the posters in their lobbies, by the mailboxes, or in the laundry room. Some may be able to help plan or sponsor alcohol-free social events. Others may volunteer to help students set up, supervise, or clean up on event nights.

Power Lines introduces students to forces within the community that influence youth decisions regarding whether or not to use alcohol. Their projects require research, and adult family

Duplicating this page is illegal. Do not copy this material without written permission from the publisher.

members can support student work by both consenting to be interviewed as community resource people and participating in polls conducted by students. It is also nice to invite parents and guardians to their children's project presentations in class, and these presentations may be expanded to create a larger event, similar to the *Slick Tracy* Poster Fair. Videotaped presentations and digital slide shows created by students might be displayed online, with an e-mail inviting families and community members to view them.

In *Class Action,* students benefit greatly from the support of any family members who are lawyers, judges, or others with legal expertise and who are available to coach them through the preparation of their cases. Some parents and guardians can participate as "expert witnesses," too (if they are physicians or psychologists, for example). Families may observe the mock trials and chaperone on a field trip to see actual civil cases tried in court. Videotaping the mock trials and any field trips can provide a way for parents with busy daytime schedules to learn more about these events.

What Types of Outreach Activities Could Draw More Families into the Program?

Formal networking, informal networking, school networking, need-based networking, and identity-based networking can all provide access to the families you want to reach.

1. **Formal networking: PTAs, PTOs, and other parent organizations**

   Preexisting parent associations provide a good way to

   • generate parent awareness and enthusiasm

   • access sponsorship for special events

   • disseminate information

2. **Informal networking: public gathering spots**

   Tap into places that are already part of many families' routines. Which ones might allow you to post or set out print materials, such as Poster Fair flyers, fact sheets about underage drinking

Duplicating this page is illegal. Do not copy this material without written permission from the publisher.

issues and Project Northland, or invitations to special events?
Here are some suggestions for getting started:

- gyms, sports facilities, and health clubs

- barbershops and hair salons

- grocery stores

- coffee shops and drive-through kiosks

- message boards

- community centers

- doctors' offices, particularly in the late summer when
  many students go in for physicals required by their athletic
  leagues

 PROGRAM TIP

At grocery stores, bag stuffing offers an informal networking opportunity.
Arrangements can be made for teens to bag customers' purchases and include
a Project Northland flyer in each bag. Alternatively, students can staple the flyers
to grocery bags at school, and school staff can return the prepared bags for the
store to use.

Another informal networking opportunity, especially in small towns, is to work
with local utility companies to have them include a message with their monthly
statements. For example, a message like "Watch for *Slick Tracy,* beginning this
month with sixth grade at Central Middle School!" could be inserted on a paper
strip or printed directly onto the water company's statement.

3. **School networking: message boards and newsletters,
   both in print and online**

   School newsletters need copy. You have it:

   - Let parents know when Project Northland is coming.

   - Post program highlights.

   - Announce special events.

   - Invite the community.

   - Post contact information.

   - Publicize interesting and surprising facts.

   - Ask provocative questions ("What drug is most dangerous
     and most commonly used by teens?").

   - Trumpet positive program outcomes.

Duplicating this page is illegal. Do not copy this material without written permission from the publisher.

School bulletin boards and electronic message boards are also good places to post Project Northland information and flyers.

4. **Need-based networking: groups for the parents of students with special needs**

Parents whose kids have special needs tend to be involved at school. Meetings that bring groups of these parents together provide good settings for introducing yourself, publicizing Project Northland, and recruiting volunteers. You might be able to get the word out through these groups' newsletters or e-mail updates, too.

Think broadly when considering special needs. Your community may include groups of families whose special needs involve developmental delay, ADD/ADHD, gifted and talented, autism, physical disability, deafness, blindness, chronic illness, cognitive disability, or other special needs.

5. **Identity-based networking: faith- or ethnicity-based groups**

While some of the special needs described above may overlap with identity, there are other identity groups that can also offer volunteers, sponsors, and other resources. These may include

- ethnic identity groups
- faith groups, such as churches, mosques, synagogues, and their youth groups
- Masons, who have their own youth programs

 PROFESSIONAL HIGHLIGHT

"When asked about the best ways to get information out to parents on alcohol use prevention, 20 to 34 percent of parents from the sixth-grade program year suggested the following: through programs or workshops, through school newsletters, by sending suggestions for preventing use, and by mailing directly to parents. Thirty-four percent of parents surveyed during the seventh-grade year suggested school newsletters as the best way. Fifteen percent or more suggested literature (i.e., books, magazines, brochures, handouts), programs or workshops, mailing directly to parents, and the Internet or e-mail. Finally, 20 to 27 percent of parents from the eighth grade suggested mail directly to parents and through school newsletters."

WILDER RESEARCH (MINNESOTA)

Duplicating this page is illegal. Do not copy this material without written permission from the publisher.

- groups like FFA and 4-H
- civic groups like the local Lions Club and Rotary
- military groups like VFW groups

Summary

Prevention programs come and go, but the ones that stay are the ones that work. These are the ones that bring families into dialogue with one another and into partnership with their children, the school, and the community. Project Northland owes much of its outstanding track record to its effective family involvement components, so make the most of these. When you involve families through good and frequent communication, opportunities for involvement, and positive feedback, you attract many who will become supporters, advocates, volunteers, and donors who help keep your program strong.

. . .

Duplicating this page is illegal. Do not copy this material without written permission from the publisher.

91

Community Mobilization

This chapter will help you understand how to organize and work with members of the community. Community coalitions can support Project Northland by increasing its base of supporters, providing additional resources, and opening new doors to community access. As you build community connections over time, you will learn which of the ideas suggested in this chapter are most feasible, useful, and worthy of the energy required to implement them as part of your program.

▶▶ *What You Will Learn in Chapter 8:*

- What is a community coalition?
- How can communities support Project Northland?
- How to effectively engage volunteers

What Is a Community Coalition?

A community coalition is a group of people who work together to achieve one or more community goals. One source defines it as "a collaborative union of individuals and groups working together to achieve a shared goal."[1] Successful coalitions include individuals and organizations representing diverse interests. Members are typically invited to join, rather than elected or appointed, though an invited organization may designate which of its staff will participate. Coalition goals typically include

- reducing alcohol, tobacco, and drug use and violence
- involving parents and other community members to support prevention efforts
- supporting school goals for academic success
- supporting community efforts to reduce crime and problem behaviors

Duplicating this page is illegal. Do not copy this material without written permission from the publisher.

What Indicators May Help Predict a Coalition's Success?

There are several indicators that can help you determine whether or not a coalition is likely to be effective. These help a group to coalesce, or come together, and support a sense of community:

■ **Sense of membership:** Individuals must feel they belong to the community and/or have an investment in the ideals of the coalition.

■ **Mutual importance:** Individuals believe that they are valued by the group, and they value their participation in the group and the contributions of other members.

■ **Shared views:** While not all members will agree on all things, there is a general convergence related to the group's goals and objectives.

■ **Bonding/networking:** Coalition members receive some intrinsic value from the experience, whether it's a sense of belonging, an opportunity to be among like-minded individuals, or the opportunity to advance professionally, politically, or personally.

■ **Mutual responsibility for the community:** Group members have a sense that they are integral to the health and wellness of their community and can be part of the solution.[2]

■ **A form of leadership that is mutually agreeable to its members:** Community coalitions require committed leadership. Many, if not most, community coalitions function without their own staffing. They utilize the time and talents of partner agency staff and a pool of volunteers. Such contributions are an "in-kind" match, an exchange of human capital or resources, rather than cash. While many coalitions eventually become private/nonprofit organizations (501(c)(3) tax exempt), many continue to function under the fiscal authority of an existing organization, such as a social service agency, school or school district, city or county government, or faith-based organization.

Duplicating this page is illegal. Do not copy this material without written permission from the publisher.

These indicators may be considered as building blocks. If you choose to help initiate a new community coalition, you will want to consider these same factors in recruiting and working with coalition members. If you get to take part in the formation of the coalition, you can use an understanding of these indicators to help form and guide it to be effective.

What Do Community Coalitions Do?

Community assessment, capacity building, strategic planning, implementing plans, and evaluating outcomes are all essentials of coalition work. Assessment is the process of determining the community's prevention needs. Capacity building improves the coalition's capabilities by developing resources. After these steps, the coalition is ready to develop, implement, and evaluate strategic plans for using their resources to address their needs.

How Do Coalitions Operate?

Coalition members meet regularly to review data, target needs, develop plans, and implement strategies to effectively reduce underage alcohol use or achieve any other targeted goals. Typically, coalitions meet on a monthly or quarterly basis. The activities and needs of the coalition will dictate the amount of face-to-face time members need.

Many coalitions function effectively by using online and telephone conferencing options, list servers, and Web links to accomplish tasks once reserved for meeting time. Keep in mind, though, that while we are fast moving into a more tech-savvy society, many people still prefer traditional "face time" with like-minded peers. Balance is important and should be considered as you plan how your coalition will communicate. You may want to begin by using multiple methods—assessing the needs, interests, and goals of the coalition's members as you move ahead—to learn how best to communicate with them both as individuals and as a board.

Duplicating this page is illegal. Do not copy this material without written permission from the publisher.

Coalition meetings are typically sixty to ninety minutes, and they should be directed to concerns relating to the identified issue: teen alcohol use. A coalition operates according to the energy and desires of its members. In many coalitions, members create task groups when two or more want to work on a specific project, activity, or goal. Task groups, or subcommittees, allow the processes to go forward with minimal disruption to the overarching strategic plan of the coalition. When subcommittees are used, they should report back with updates and results to the larger group, creating continuity and buy-in.

What Are Some Ways to Avoid Common Pitfalls of Coalition Work?

■ **To stay on track, maintain leadership that is clear and firm.** It is important for the coalition's leader to consider the members' depth and breadth of understanding of the project and related issues as well as their commitment to staying on track. It might be best to assume that most coalition members will not have the level of knowledge, insight, or commitment that the coalition coordinator does regarding effective prevention strategies, the key objectives of the project, or the strategic plan.

Exercise careful judgment in how you use even the most capable of partners to ensure that the partner's needs and interests do not inadvertently interfere or contrast with those of the project. More than one coalition has become "hijacked" by well-meaning members who shift focus onto pet projects or the "issue du jour."

■ **Stay current, but maintain focus on your original long-term goals.** New trends will emerge, yet the coalition will need to maintain its focus on defined long-term goals and avoid chasing the inevitable hot topic of the day. Coalitions that focused on alcohol use have found they could demonstrate considerably lower rates of methamphetamine and other substance use.

Duplicating this page is illegal. Do not copy this material without written permission from the publisher.

Many coalitions use a risk/protective factor approach. The coalition's broad mission is to reduce risks that lead to problem behaviors and promote protective assets to build resiliency among youth, adults, families, and systems. Within this model, subcommittees or task groups can focus on emerging issues and not derail the broader coalition work. All efforts will then be toward a common goal while incorporating creative and innovative approaches.

■ **Get to know the individual coalition members.** What are their specific interests and reasons for helping to prevent underage drinking? What is the spark, passion, or personal experience that brings them to the coalition? What personal or political goals do they bring to the work? It is helpful for the coordinator to know why each person is there and how his or her goals fit with the group's intentions.

Where Can I Learn More about Community Coalitions?

There are many resources available to help develop a new coalition, or even to rejuvenate a tired, complacent one. A few examples follow:

PROFESSIONAL HIGHLIGHT

"Our original grant had good results. We wanted to continue and expand, so we wrote a second grant. With the second grant, it became more of a community effort with the coalition."

COMMUNITY COALITION COORDINATOR (MINNESOTA)

- Community Anti-Drug Coalitions of America (CADCA) is a 501(c)(3) nonprofit organization that works to strengthen the capacity of community coalitions in their effort to create and maintain safe, healthy, and drug-free communities. CADCA supports its members with training and technical assistance, public policy advocacy, media strategies and marketing programs, conferences, and special events.

- Communities That Care (CTC) is a system developed by J. David Hawkins and Richard F. Catalano that empowers communities to use advances from prevention science to guide their prevention efforts. Materials are publicly available for download from the SAMHSA Web site.[3]

- SAMHSA's Prevention Platform is an online resource developed by the Center for Substance Abuse Prevention (CSAP).

Duplicating this page is illegal. Do not copy this material without written permission from the publisher.

The site includes a format to effectively navigate the Strategic Prevention Framework.[4] Those who register have access to an abundance of information and tools designed to assist in the key areas of assessment, capacity building, planning, implementation, and evaluation.

More information about these and other resources is provided on the CD-ROM.

How Can Communities Support Project Northland?

Environmental Prevention Efforts Supported the First Project Northland Communities

A key focus of the Project Northland authors' community coalition work was to incorporate environmental strategies to reduce access to alcohol by changing the policies, practices, and ordinances of communities, agencies, merchants, and police. Communitywide task forces emphasized collaboration with existing organizations and links with local groups to directly influence underage drinking. This included discussions with local alcohol merchants about their alcohol-related policies concerning young people and educating them on policies such as identification checks and legal consequences for selling alcohol to minors.

Their strategies included the following:

- Responsible Beverage Service training in all communities

- compliance checks

- reducing youth access at community festivals

- policies to limit alcohol access in private homes

- ordinance changes, such as noisy assembly laws

 PROGRAM TIP

Before community organizing, the authors' team introduced other environmental strategies, such as community education, alcohol-free alternative activities for teens, and community service activities. During this earlier phase, the provision of alcohol-free youth activities was particularly successful.

Duplicating this page is illegal. Do not copy this material without written permission from the publisher.

Community organizing mobilized the community's members to support, initiate, and establish policies to reduce youth access to alcohol in a systematic way:

■ **Action plans** were developed by teams of community members to indicate the methods and strategies they would use to decrease the commercial availability of alcohol to teens in liquor stores, bars, and convenience stores. Teams received training on policy development and were provided with a menu of potential actions.

■ **These performance objectives were developed:**

- The community will develop capacity to address the issue of underage access to and use of alcohol.

- The community will reduce the number of commercial sources for alcohol that are available to adolescents.

- Policymakers and city government will strengthen the communities' alcohol policies and ordinances to prevent youth access to alcohol.

- The police and owners of retail stores will enforce policies, ordinances, and laws regarding underage drinking.

■ **Education** was key to sustaining policy achievements. Citizens and government officials needed to be aware of policies, and the law enforcement agencies needed to be responsible for their enforcement.

■ **Action teams brainstormed initiatives.** They used three questions to select initiatives with the greatest potential for environmental impact:

1. How and where do students obtain alcohol?
2. What barriers can communities create to keep students from obtaining alcohol?
3. How will my community know if changes take place at the community level?

PROFESSIONAL HIGHLIGHT

"Family and community interventions that have been shown to be effective included a focus on limiting youth access to alcohol . . . Such approaches need to include not only the adoption of laws and ordinances, but also their enforcement and the development of a strong social norm that supports the intent of such legislation.

For example, Project Northland . . . included efforts to reduce underage access to alcohol, and . . . these efforts were found to have significant effects on reducing drinking." [6]

■ **Action teams used this framework** in considering the third question above and maintaining the focus on environmental change:

- change targets groups, not individuals
- change targets key institutions, key businesses, or whole communities
- change provides long-term solutions that will benefit students both now and in the future [5]

■ **Training was extended to community institutions.** Each community offered Responsible Beverage Service training for managers of bars and liquor stores. This training included specific policy options to implement within their stores to reduce youth access to alcohol. Engaging merchants in ownership of this issue promotes community efficacy and potential support for future initiatives around youth access.

■ **Consensus and enforcement**—the purpose of these community interventions was to foster community adoption of institutional or policy solutions to underage drinking, separate from the educational strategies directed at the adolescents. To be effective, alcohol policies need to be rigorously enforced, which was more likely to occur with a strong public consensus.

■ **Several strategies were used to encourage enforcement of existing policies and to encourage the adoption of new policies.** Educational compliance checks (not for prosecution) of age-of-sale laws, coordinated with local law enforcement, were conducted to inform the communities and local merchants of the ease with which underage youth could purchase alcohol. Letters were sent to merchants from the local law enforcement agency, notifying them of the compliance checks and the failure of staff to enforce age-of-sale laws. Merchants were warned that checks would occur again, at random.

Successive compliance checks were conducted with penalties attached. The community action teams provided their compli-

Duplicating this page is illegal. Do not copy this material without written permission from the publisher.

ance check results to evidence the lack of enforcement for existing laws. The evidence was leveraged with city councils to initiate the adoption of communitywide compliance check ordinances and Responsible Beverage Service training as well as administrative penalties for businesses that failed to comply with age-of-sale laws.

 PROGRAM TIP

To conduct compliance checks in your community, you may want to use the authors' materials as a reference. These are found on the CD-ROM.

- **Media advocacy** also played a role in defining the community's health agenda by

  - raising the public profile of issues by bringing them to the attention of the community

  - conferring importance and legitimacy to the issues as relevant to community concerns

  - providing frameworks of meaning within which issues are better understood

  - disseminating public health information widely

  Media involvement increased the visibility of the alcohol access issue and environmental strategy options in the community. It supported the community action teams' agendas.

- **Youth action teams** were formed to accomplish the youth development objectives. These teams consisted of students who voluntarily participated in training sessions and project planning to reduce teenage alcohol use in their communities. An adult counselor was hired to work with each youth action team, and students from all Project Northland schools gathered at retreat centers for daylong training. Students from all schools were brought together to share their experiences and ideas, to motivate each other to take action in their communities, and to

Duplicating this page is illegal. Do not copy this material without written permission from the publisher.

101

learn the skills needed to address environmental conditions. The training sessions focused on increasing knowledge about environmental factors, options for revising school policies, enforcement options, and building students' confidence working on this issue. The sessions exposed students to peers who had taken action in their communities, and youth speakers were invited to share their stories.

Upon their return to the communities, youth action teams met with their adult coordinators to identify the environmental conditions contributing to underage alcohol use in their own communities. Each team then explored strategies to address these conditions. Students were given the opportunity to choose projects that addressed the problem and changed something in the environment. They tested project ideas for feasibility and created action plans. Adult coordinators provided resources to keep the youth action teams on track with their projects. The youth action teams were designed to be led by the students. The adult coordinator's role was to guide the students and support their activities.

Youth action teams were given the opportunity to apply for mini-grants to help implement their projects. This system was chosen to teach students about grant writing, timelines, and budgeting. On the grant application, they were also asked to demonstrate collaborative efforts within community organizations. These efforts increased the students' exposure, ownership, and positive recognition.

An important part of Project Northland's youth development component was to increase positive recognition for teens in the community. The media served as the main vehicle for providing this recognition. Press releases by and about the students featured their efforts. Featured highlights included students' recommendations to their communities for how to reduce underage alcohol use and student planning of alcohol-free activities for their peers. Positive recognition of students and their activities helped recruit additional students to the

PROFESSIONAL HIGHLIGHT

"Some successful programs, like Project Northland . . . made use of community media as part of a multifaceted campaign." [7]

Duplicating this page is illegal. Do not copy this material without written permission from the publisher.

action teams. Student leaders served as role models for students in lower grades by speaking in classrooms and at assemblies.

Prom, homecoming, and graduation are key times of the year when students tend to drink alcohol and community members tend to overlook underage drinking. Youth action teams were encouraged to identify important environmental conditions related to these events and plan to address those conditions. Mini-grants were given for projects such as homecoming tailgate parties, postprom parties, preprom dinners, and graduation celebrations. The policies developed for these events explicitly stated the expectations for attendees and specific consequences that would occur if a student was caught drinking.

 PROGRAM TIP

Prom time offers many opportunities for creative prevention efforts. Safety messages can be printed on prom tickets and on stickers for florists to use on their boxes for corsages and boutonnieres. Owners of tuxedo and limousine rentals, as well as hair salons and other businesses, can be enlisted to help spread safety messages, too.

Community support contributed greatly to the success of these events. Students proved that they were committed to working on the issue and educated community groups about the need for their involvement. Community members, impressed with the students' initiative, donated items such as door prizes and food, gave volunteer support, and contributed to media coverage. Many of these events became annual celebrations because of the normative shift that occurred during one successful year.

These community interventions early in Project Northland's implementation history affected environmental prevention through community and organizational-level change. They also empowered the at-risk group itself—the adolescents—to make changes in circumstances important to their lives and their health.

Duplicating this page is illegal. Do not copy this material without written permission from the publisher.

Methods and Strategies for Youth Development

METHOD	STRATEGIES
Youth development and skill development	• Form youth action teams in the schools with an adult liaison to support the groups. • Train students in public participation and action strategies. • Have youth action teams plan projects and activities to address concerns.
Incentives	• Increase positive recognition of teens in the community.
Modeling	• Expose students to same-age peers who have taken action in their communities.
Opportunities	• Establish a grant-making system for students to receive funds for projects.
Peer participation	• Recruit students for youth action teams. • Create student-led teams.
Norms for nonuse	• Help students plan alcohol-free events and activities.

Strategies that focus on making community changes around access to alcohol exemplify one way to create communitywide change. In other communities, local needs, culture, norms, and climate help indicate the best focus and approach for coalitions to use.

Coalitions Can Help Launch Project Northland

In an advisory capacity, the coalition may help identify key stakeholders and enlist their support. In cases where Project Northland had been the passion of a key board member, that person has worked to influence school boards, city councils, review boards, recovery groups, and law enforcement associations to ensure that the program would be used to address the community's needs.

Coalitions Can Help Build Capacity

The capacity of a coalition is defined by the talents and resources of its members and affiliates. Therefore, effective coalitions include a broad spectrum of experience and perspective. A federally supported program

Duplicating this page is illegal. Do not copy this material without written permission from the publisher.

called the Drug Free Communities (DFC) Support Program offers grant funds to community coalitions that designate drug- and alcohol-use prevention as their primary focus. Promoting a model that has been proven effective across the country, DFC coalitions demonstrate substantial participation from volunteer leaders in their communities.

These coalitions include representation from each of the following twelve sectors:

1. youth (an individual eighteen or under)

2. parents

3. business community

4. media

5. school

6. youth-serving organizations

7. law enforcement agencies

8. religious or fraternal organizations

9. civic and volunteer groups

10. health care professionals

11. state, local, or tribal governmental agencies with expertise in the field of substance abuse

12. other organizations involved in reducing substance abuse

The importance of youth representation warrants emphasis. In keeping with the fundamentals of positive youth development, and to avoid "tokenism," a coalition should include a broad cross-section of youth. Just as one adult could not speak for the whole community, a single youth should not be expected to represent the full spectrum of youth interests, personalities, and experiences. Some coalitions engage an established youth-directed body as an ad-hoc committee of the coalition, and then a sample of youth from this group—maybe one to three representatives—function as liaisons with the group, rather than as individual decision makers.

PROFESSIONAL HIGHLIGHT

"I have the two biggest counties, with 1,200 students in three grade levels. Our rural coalition has included 300 members—law enforcement, students, people from medicine, education, and counseling; there were politicians involved two years ago."

SUBSTANCE ABUSE COUNCIL PROGRAM DIRECTOR (TEXAS)

Duplicating this page is illegal. Do not copy this material without written permission from the publisher.

When building or expanding your coalition, keep in mind the various sectors you want represented and how best to align your needs with theirs. The following categories may be useful:

- **Youth:** Middle, high school, and alternative school students; student leaders; youth who've accessed services; and youth who have been on probation all provide unique perspectives.

- **Parents:** Those affiliated with traditional parent organizations, parents of youth in services, and foster parents offer a range of relevant background experiences.

- **Business community:** The stakeholders in this category include employers in general and employers of youth, business owners—including those that sell alcohol—donors, decision makers in the community, chamber of commerce members, job skills trainers, and members of service clubs such as Rotary, Kiwanis, and Lions Club.

- **Media:** Include the full spectrum of school and community newspapers, radio, network or public access TV, and bloggers in this category.

- **School administrators:** Consider Safe and Drug-Free Schools coordinators, special education directors, curriculum directors, school counselors, assistant principals, behavior specialists, prevention and intervention specialists, school social workers, school board members, and others.

- **Youth-serving organizations:** After-school staff, coaches, youth club advisers, and the coordinators and directors of local youth-serving organizations outside of school are all invested in the future of young people.

- **Law enforcement:** Patrol officers, juvenile crime detectives, school resource officers, school and college security personnel, juvenile judges, probation officers, and ATOD diversion court coordinators are all part of the solution.

Duplicating this page is illegal. Do not copy this material without written permission from the publisher.

- **Faith-based organizations:** Religious leaders, youth pastors, Young Life or other nondenominational youth groups, ministerial associations, and chaplains all offer meaningful contributions. Find out who holds the most sway among the targeted population.

- **Health care professionals:** Mental health and chemical dependency specialists, pediatricians, emergency room staff, and public health personnel offer valuable perspectives.

- **Family services and at-risk youth program personnel** may contribute unique insights.

- **The recovery community:** This includes Alcoholics Anonymous, Narcotics Anonymous, Alateen, Al-Anon, and other Twelve Step groups. These include many individuals who bring a special passion to their coalition work.

RESEARCH FACT

Communities May Want to Restrict Alcohol Advertising

Research clearly indicates that alcohol advertising and marketing significantly impact youth alcohol use. Alcohol advertising creates and reinforces positive beliefs about alcohol use. This, in turn, increases teens' intention to use alcohol.[8] Alcohol advertising encourages youth to drink.[9]

One study concluded that for each additional ad a young person saw above the monthly average of twenty-three, he or she drank 1 percent more.[10] For each additional dollar per capita spent on alcohol advertising in a local market above the national average of $6.80, young people drank 3 percent more. Another study of approximately 2,000 New Hampshire middle school students who had never used alcohol showed that ownership of alcohol-branded merchandise was significantly associated with increased likelihood of having initiated drinking at follow-up.[11]

Project Northland researchers examined outdoor alcohol advertisements within 1,500 feet of sixty-three school sites. A total of 931 alcohol advertisements were found. Results showed that exposure to alcohol advertising in the sixth grade was significantly associated with subsequent intentions to use alcohol in the eighth grade. This association held even when taking into account sixth graders who had never used alcohol.[12]

Duplicating this page is illegal. Do not copy this material without written permission from the publisher.

Coalitions Can Help with Community Assessment

Chapter 3 of this manual, with its accompanying CD-ROM materials, offers some information on community assessment. In community work, as in all prevention programming, it is important to accurately define the scope of the problem you seek to address. An initial step is to define the geographic boundaries of the effort. Is the coalition addressing a single neighborhood, a whole city, or a larger area such as a whole county or tribal areas? Often, coalitions affiliated with Project Northland programs focus on a specific school district service area.

However the geographic boundaries are defined, the membership of a coalition should match the demographics of the community, including race and ethnicity, interest groups, service providers, and decision makers. Consider the following in identifying the diverse populations within your community:

- What races/ethnicities are represented in your schools?

- Do you have a growing immigrant population?

- Are there rural as well as developed areas to be represented?

- Are there special populations to consider, such as seniors, industry-related groups, prisons, colleges, or tribal groups?

Once geographic boundaries are determined, coalitions must gather and analyze data. Data provides a clear, objective view of the community. Data also comes in a variety of forms, and it ranges in terms of reliability. An anonymous author once said, "Statistics can be made to prove anything, even the truth," but most social scientists—and funders—believe energies should be spent on those issues that are statistically relevant to the population.

Data analysis will help you identify key risk and protective factors to target for planning coalition work to serve the community. As they grow up, youth are exposed to a number of factors that may either increase or decrease their likelihood of abusing alcohol or engaging in other delinquent behavior. These are referred to as "risk factors" and "protective factors."

Duplicating this page is illegal. Do not copy this material without written permission from the publisher.

Risk factors are any circumstances that may increase youths' likelihood of engaging in risky behaviors. Conversely, protective factors are any circumstances that promote healthy youth behaviors and decrease the chance that youth will engage in risky behaviors. Risk factors and protective factors are often organized into five categories or domains:

- individual
- family
- school
- peer group
- community

The assessment process will lead you to discover which risk and protective factors may be influencing your community's youth. Your coalition will want to explore available data to determine the extent of impact those risk and protective factors are having and their influence on the issues you have identified as your focus. Once you have identified the risk and protective factors to be addressed, you can turn your efforts to selecting proven programs and strategies that effectively address them.

For most purposes of a Project Northland coalition, data sources are going to be those relevant to the service area within your targeted geographic boundaries. Regional, state, and national data will help you compare your community's data to the larger group and similar communities. Some likely sources of useful data are

- youth risk behavior surveys
- enrollment in chemical dependency programs
- hospital/ER admission data
- public health vital statistics
- law enforcement response logs
- juvenile justice crime data
- DUI/DWI arrest rates
- alcohol density reports
- school attendance and dropout rates
- school disciplinary data

Duplicating this page is illegal. Do not copy this material without written permission from the publisher.

The data should paint a clear picture of the real and defensible needs in your area. This process of collecting and analyzing data will lead you to select demographics. For example, your community strategies might target youth, parents, schools, and/or the community as a whole.

Many coalitions will identify one or two groups on which to focus in the early years of coalition work. For instance, in working with parents, a coalition may choose strategies that inform parents with accurate and consistent information on health and legal consequences of alcohol/drug use on youth, thus increasing the parents' capacity to establish expectations and rules for their children.

 PROGRAM TIP

Instructions and resources for implementing these classic Project Northland interventions are provided on the CD-ROM:

- Form a **student activity group.** This is a student-led group, supervised by an adult, that plans alcohol-free social activities for teens. The group provides teens with social support to avoid drinking alcohol and helps increase their awareness of alternatives to drinking.

- Hold an *Amazing Alternatives* **Fun Night.** This event connects teens, parents, and other family and community members with the school for entertainment, socializing, and learning. It provides a model for alcohol-free fun where adults interact with their teens and each other to learn about adolescent alcohol use and healthy alternatives.

- Award **gold cards.** This program rewards students who agree not to use alcohol, tobacco, and other drugs, and it encourages their academic achievement, community service, and participation in extracurricular activities. Coalition members, school staff, or a task force work with local businesses willing to donate money, discounts, coupons, or merchandise as club rewards, and they establish criteria for students to earn and maintain card club membership.

Other Ways Coalition Members Can Support Project Northland

As strategy partners, coalition members may be involved directly in classroom implementation. Consider the following opportunities:

- A retired teacher may volunteer to support delivery of the curriculum by "tag teaming" with the teacher. This coalition

Duplicating this page is illegal. Do not copy this material without written permission from the publisher.

member may help with everything from making copies of handouts to delivering the program in classrooms (with a teacher providing appropriate management support).

- A school resource officer knows that law enforcement colleagues have presented D.A.R.E. but wants to do something backed by evidence that it will help in middle schools. Project Northland can enable the police department to continue this tradition of classroom delivery while employing strategies that have been proven effective.

- Youth advocates—such as counselors, advisers, recreation staff, and others—may assist with planning and delivering Peer Leader training for *Slick Tracy* and *Amazing Alternatives*. These individuals bring experience and expertise in positive youth development. They can help this select group of young people grow successfully into their new role as Peer Leaders and open doors to additional youth leadership opportunities for them in the future.

- Partnering with a college or university will open up access to students studying education, health promotion, psychology, and/or social work. Communities have found great opportunities to engage older youth as role models for helping to implement curriculum or in designing or delivering the Peer Leader training experiences.

- Coalition members can showcase student projects from *Slick Tracy* and *Power Lines*. Consider having the coalition host the *Slick Tracy* Poster Fair, complete with guest speakers, prizes, and refreshments.

There are also many ways that coalition members can participate as collateral support to the classroom-based programs. With each of the curricula—*Slick Tracy, Amazing Alternatives, Power Lines,* and *Class Action*—there are multiple opportunities for meaningful involvement without burdening coalition members with the traditional demands of implementing curriculum:

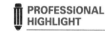

PROFESSIONAL HIGHLIGHT

"Our office does a lot of prep for the teachers. We've created crates for classroom teachers with curriculum, supplies, copies of the student materials, laminated game cards, etc. The coalition's office maintains these."

COMMUNITY COALITION DIRECTOR (ILLINOIS)

Duplicating this page is illegal. Do not copy this material without written permission from the publisher.

PROFESSIONAL HIGHLIGHT

"We've assembled packets with background materials for specific Power Lines *projects. These include video clips, people resources in the community—such as a judge or a pediatrician to discuss FAS—and other resources for the teacher."*

COMMUNITY COALITION DIRECTOR (ILLINOIS)

- Local businesses may sponsor a sixth-grade class by under-writing the cost of their *Slick Tracy* comic books. Insurance agents have been particularly amenable to this initiative, as they know all too well the cost of alcohol abuse. A sticker with the agent's name may be applied to the cover with a message such as "The *Slick Tracy* participation of Mr. Williams's class is supported by Ellen Greene of Acme Insurance." Business partners may be interested in offer-ing support with other materials, too, such as incentive prizes, poster and project supplies, Peer Leader training materials, refreshments, curriculum materials for new teachers, and more.

- For *Power Lines,* many of the "experts" that eighth graders will need to interview may be represented within the coalition. Helping to connect coalition members with these students will facilitate project development and encourage meaningful and appropriate involvement by the adult representatives.

- The coalition could host a special Project Northland gradu-ation—perhaps incorporating presentation of *Power Lines* projects—and invite community members and the media. This event could take place at the end of either *Power Lines* or *Class Action,* and it may be designed in a way to help transition middle school students to their new high school.

- Coalition members may also be—or have family members who are—lawyers and judges who can volunteer or recruit volunteers. For example, bar association volunteers have sometimes helped students prepare their cases for *Class Action.* Also, college and graduate school professors may be interested in having their students help with the program.

- Coalition members may invite youth to present their posters, projects, or presentations to service clubs, school boards, city councils, or county planning boards. This reinforces the social influence/advocacy model and brings

Duplicating this page is illegal. Do not copy this material without written permission from the publisher.

young people further into contact with the systems that influence community behavior.

• Coalition members can work to support the National Minimum Drinking Age Act, maintaining the minimum legal drinking age of twenty-one.

RESEARCH FACT

Communities That Support the Minimum Drinking Age Act Save Lives

Since the National Minimum Drinking Age Act (NMDAA) established twenty-one as the minimum legal drinking age, the National Highway Traffic Safety Administration has shown that drunken driving fatalities have decreased by 13 percent among eighteen- to twenty-year-olds.[13] Other studies have shown the age twenty-one drinking law has also reduced youth drinking in general.[14] In addition, studies have shown that during the time when some states had a lower minimum drinking age, the suicide rate of eighteen- to twenty-year-olds was higher in states with a minimum legal drinking age below twenty-one.[15] In fact, a review of existing programs and policies indicates that increasing the legal age for purchase and consumption of alcohol to age twenty-one has been the most successful campaign to reduce drinking among teenagers and young adults.[16]

Despite subsequent debate about lowering the drinking age to eighteen to lower binge drinking among underage youth, higher rates of drinking among youth and young adults is not due to having a high minimum legal drinking age of twenty-one, but due to lack of enforcement of the current law.[17] The legal minimum drinking age of twenty-one helps prevent motor-vehicle traffic crashes, as well as alcohol-related injuries, suicide, homicide, assault, drowning, and other problems among teenagers and young adults. Studies of effects associated with lowering New Zealand's legal drinking age from twenty to eighteen showed an increase in the number of intoxicated eighteen- and nineteen-year-olds—as well as the number of intoxicated fifteen- to seventeen-year-olds—admitted to emergency rooms.[18]

How to Effectively Engage Volunteers

Celebrating the Participation of Each Individual Helps Keep Everyone Connected

When engaging coalition members, be mindful of some basic tenets regarding the "care and feeding" of volunteers. These people, like anyone else, want to be put to good use and believe they have something to contribute. Otherwise, they wouldn't be there. Investigate the resources each person brings to your team. Also, remember that not everyone gives equally or in the same way.

Duplicating this page is illegal. Do not copy this material without written permission from the publisher.

Find out both the "traditional" and "nontraditional" skills of each coalition member. An involved parent might also offer the services of his or her own catering business; the principal's wife might be a professor with university students seeking evaluative research experience; the art teacher might have a graphic design business on the side; a coach might be willing to share access to passenger vans as needed. When building capacity, it helps to think outside of the proverbial box!

Regardless of how greatly (or minimally) the coalition and its members participate, be sure to recognize their contributions. Appreciative gestures go a long way to validate givers and keep them coming back. Such gestures may include thank-you letters, certificates, cards from students, an annual volunteer reception, printed acknowledgment in newsletters or programs for special events, and more. Always keep in mind that the involvement of coalition members is in addition to their other responsibilities.

Successful coalition coordinators have a bag of tricks to keep things interesting, new, and meaningful for volunteers. People want to contribute, yet there are often many interests competing for their limited time. Volunteers need to experience some intrinsic gain and/or believe that they are integral to the project in order to stay connected. Here are some tips from established coalitions:

■ **Mentors:** When new coalition members join, match them with an experienced member to help them learn the ropes.

■ **"Breakfast of Champions":** Hold an annual breakfast meeting or after-school reception to celebrate successes and distribute thoughtful awards. Use this event to bond within the group. You might broaden your network by inviting others from the community.

■ **Volunteer survival kits:** Give a clever, fun, and cost-effective gift to amuse volunteers and recognize the multitude of talents and experience they bring to the group. For example, place these items in a plastic bag with the following label (shown on the next page).

Duplicating this page is illegal. Do not copy this material without written permission from the publisher.

VOLUNTEER KIT

- **MARBLES** in case someone says you've lost yours!

- **A BAND-AID** because you are called in to fix the scrapes.

- **AN ERASER** to clean up those mistakes.

- **A PENNY** so you'll never have to say, "I'm broke."

- **A RUBBER BAND** to stretch beyond your limits.

- **A PAPER CLIP** to keep things from falling apart.

- **A (HERSHEY'S) HUG** to say thanks!

- **A (HERSHEY'S) KISS** because the hug left you wanting more!

■ **Use your creativity** to make it fun, and include items to reflect and respond to the personality of the community and individual members. For example:

- Penny for your thoughts
- Paper clip to help you hold it together
- Chocolate mints because, as the saying goes, you're worth a mint!

■ **Coffee mugs:** Although it requires a little investment, the gesture of creating personalized mugs and keeping them at the coalition's meeting place demonstrates value and creates connections to a shared space. Having one's own mug at each meeting reinforces the sense of belonging. These also function as an easy visual reminder of who is in attendance and what their names are. You can put small prizes in mugs from time to time, to recognize special efforts of individual coalition members or to commemorate milestones such as birthdays and special accomplishments.

Duplicating this page is illegal. Do not copy this material without written permission from the publisher.

■ **Star features:** Consider highlighting a different coalition member each month or quarter in your newsletter. Conduct an informal interview of the individual and write a short piece that includes some information outside their professional or coalition life, such as hobbies, favorite sports teams, talents, dream vacation, or family. This helps coalition members see themselves and others as more than representatives on the board, and it takes the coalition's sense of community to another level. This, in turn, increases commitment to the group. It may also serve you well in extending your resource list of talents represented among the group.

Avoiding Under- or Overutilization of Volunteers
Helps Maintain Enthusiasm

Consider your volunteers your greatest asset and, with little exception, try to reserve each one for the tasks to which they are best suited. Even the best-hearted volunteers will tire if they feel under- or overutilized.

■ **Underutilized** refers to either having people work below their capacity or not engaging them often enough for them to feel ownership of the effort. From time to time, every volunteer logs his or her hours stapling, folding, and stuffing envelopes, but assign this type of work with caution. If you have experts sitting at your table, engage them in activities that utilize their skills. These might include public speaking, advocacy, public policy work, writing, design, technology, and other talents helpful to your work.

■ **Overutilizing** a coalition member may cause her or him to burn out or believe she or he is becoming like staff to your program. A coalition member who has teaching skills may not relish the opportunity to teach Project Northland full time; maybe she or he retired to make time for other things. A successful fund-raiser or event planner may enjoy such work and give graciously, but not appreciate the expectation of being involved this way for every event.

Duplicating this page is illegal. Do not copy this material without written permission from the publisher.

Sometimes overutilization involves asking too much in terms of responsibility rather than workload. Consider the related issues likely to come up when supervising youth or other adults: transporting materials, phone expenses, mileage, and others. Also keep in mind that not all volunteers will embrace each and every task affiliated with your project. Be mindful of accommodating volunteers' needs and abilities.

Summary

Community coalitions can be great supporters of Project Northland, and community involvement greatly enhances program effectiveness. You may have the opportunity to work with an established coalition, help strengthen an existing coalition, or form a new one alongside your program. Since coalitions differ widely, as do communities, there is no "one size fits all" approach to either developing a coalition or engaging an existing one. Start by building community support upon the strengths you identified in chapter 3.

Duplicating this page is illegal. Do not copy this material without written permission from the publisher.

117

Promoting Your Program

Yours is the face and voice of Project Northland in your community. This chapter offers ideas about communicating effectively to build relationships that promote and support your program.

▶▶ *What You Will Learn in Chapter 9:*

- What modes of communication will engage the community?
- How can I communicate best with different stakeholders?
- How can I work effectively with the media?

What Modes of Communication Will Engage the Community?

To build the community connections that will launch and sustain your program, you want to communicate effectively with all the stakeholders: teachers, students, parents, administrators, school board members, business owners, public safety personnel, emergency service providers, physicians, policymakers, and other community members. These modes will shape your communications:

Introducing: Let people know what Project Northland is, why it is effective, and why it is needed.

Informing: Educate community members about the seriousness of underage alcohol use and its consequences, as well as the importance of effective prevention during middle school. Explain how preventing, delaying, and reducing alcohol use during adolescence will benefit the community.

Listening: Hear what teachers and others say, need, and want throughout the program. Respond thoughtfully, in a way that reflects your understanding of their messages.

Duplicating this page is illegal. Do not copy this material without written permission from the publisher.

Connecting: Let others know how they can get involved with Project Northland.

Publicizing: Build excitement for the program among teachers, students, parents, and other community members before the program starts.

Training: Coordinate staff training. Train Peer Leaders.

Promoting: Promote the program by announcing and celebrating its successes. Share stories and outcomes that demonstrate progress.

Thanking: Acknowledge and appreciate the work of teachers, students, volunteers, and others.

How Can I Communicate Best with Different Stakeholders?

Students

- Let students know that Project Northland is coming and when, through the use of
  - posters
  - flyers
  - e-mail alerts
  - school Web notices
  - table tents in the cafeteria
- Use these to build feelings of interest and positive anticipation: Students can look forward to comic books in class, fun events, and activities in the community.

Teachers

- Help teachers look ahead to assimilate Project Northland into their curriculum.
- Help teachers find the most convenient time of year for the project.
- Promote the program to teachers: Show them how Project Northland will not just be another obligation but a boost to

Duplicating this page is illegal. Do not copy this material without written permission from the publisher.

teachers' other work, a program that could make a difference in student attendance, attention, and success in teachers' classes immediately and over time.

Parents

- Send announcements home to parents through flyers, a mention in the school newsletter or newspaper, and/or e-mails.

- Do more than send a letter letting parents know about Project Northland; get them on board by asking for volunteers and input.

- Demonstrate to members of your parent-teacher organization that Project Northland is a worthwhile program that will make a difference to their school and the families in it. Gain their support.

Administrators

- Gain administrators' support and awareness of the program.

- Build relationships with administrators.

- Help administrators realize that it is necessary for teachers to have release time for training and for teachers and students to take time to implement the program in their school.

- Help administrators see how the program can improve or enhance their school's attendance records, grades, test scores, and profile in the community.

School Board

- Gain the school board's awareness and support for the program.

- Show the school board that Project Northland can be a flagship program that builds connections between schools and students while increasing the safety of the community and the results of the schools.

Beyond the School: The Community

- Contact individual community members who may be good contacts for students working on the curriculum: potential class

Duplicating this page is illegal. Do not copy this material without written permission from the publisher.

speakers, shop owners who may display posters for alternative event nights, and so on.

- Build relationships and gain support within professional and political groups that are working toward common goals (reducing alcoholism, reducing alcohol access to underage drinkers, reducing alcohol-related fatalities). Such groups may become partners in work on *Power Lines*.

- Contact associations and organizations who have a vested interest in the program and may support it through gifts of money, publicity, time, tours, speakers, and more:
    - the local bar (lawyers') association
    - the police station
    - service clubs
    - local merchants' associations
    - faith communities

Media

- Build relationships with appropriate people (school beat, event announcements, columnists) at local/community newspapers. You may want to be able to call on these people later to ask them to write a story or a column on Project Northland activities and their impact or to list *Amazing Alternatives* event nights.

- Contact local radio stations to see if they will promote the program for free or sponsor a contest for the best alcohol-use prevention poster or alternative event.

Funders

- Let potential and existing funders know about the strengths and promise of the program.

- Keep funders up-to-date on project timelines and events.

- Invite funders to the *Slick Tracy* Poster Fair, the *Amazing Alternatives* Fun Night, and other events.

- Clip any newspaper articles about Project Northland activities or results to send to funders. If the publicity is online, e-mail links to funding contact people.

Duplicating this page is illegal. Do not copy this material without written permission from the publisher.

• Send funders evaluations and data that demonstrate progress made by your program.

How Can I Work Effectively with the Media?

What Benefits Come from Working with the Media?

Local media can help you broadcast your news and achieve your communication goals on a wider scale. Reasons to work with the media include the following:

• to raise awareness in a community about the need to reduce youth alcohol use

• to generate interest and support among policymakers and the community at large in reducing youth alcohol use

• to explain what Project Northland is and why it is a good fit for your community

• to build anticipation for upcoming Project Northland events

• to inform people of Project Northland activities and other news

• to recruit volunteers and sponsors to support your program

• to lay groundwork for broadcasting or publishing student projects

What Media Might I Engage at No Cost?

■ **Newspapers:** Daily newspapers, weekly community papers, and school papers may interview you, publish statistics or a position statement of need, update the community on Project Northland events, or describe student curriculum activities.

■ **Radio and television:** Local news programs, public access, community-supported stations, interviews on local talk shows, and school programming can all be good outlets to explain the need, describe the program, and celebrate successes.

Duplicating this page is illegal. Do not copy this material without written permission from the publisher.

Bulletins/Newsletters: Many organizations, such as religious congregations, business groups, public service agencies, and special interest groups have newsletters or bulletins in which you could publish announcements, short articles, or calls for participation at no charge.

Electronic Media: Web-based newsletters, bulletins, blogs, and other electronic media also provide many great opportunities for promoting your program.

What Are Some Strategies for Gaining Media Access?

■ **Write a media release.**

Use media releases to announce an event or report progress on a project. Send media releases to print, broadcast, and Web-based media. Reporters will rewrite the release to fit their format and needs.

Duplicating this page is illegal. Do not copy this material without written permission from the publisher.

■ **Write a letter to the editor or an opinion column.**

For example, if the city council votes against a new penalty for liquor stores that sell alcohol to minors, write to express disappointment in the council's actions. Other readers' letters and columns in response can make for a lively community debate. Extend the impact of a particular news story by encouraging parents and others involved in Project Northland to write letters to the editor on the issue. If Project Northland is already under way, you may encourage students to write letters and/or use students' projects and statements in support of your arguments.

■ **Write a monthly column.**

Propose the idea of a column to the editors of school and local newspapers. A column would help keep Project Northland and the issue of underage alcohol use in the public consciousness. You can let students, teachers, parents, administrators, or community members be guest columnists; use facts from the curriculum; or use examples from students' work.

■ **Call a news conference.**

Increase your chances of getting your news conference coverage by offering something more visually interesting than "talking heads." For example, if local law enforcement conducts compliance checks at liquor stores, display all the alcohol purchased out of compliance.

■ **Invite the media to Project Northland events.**

When you host a community launch party, *Slick Tracy* Poster Fair, *Amazing Alternatives* event, *Power Lines* project share-in, or *Class Action* mock trial, invite photographers and reporters from school and local news media to cover the event.

■ **Be a news source.**

Gather statistics on youth alcohol use in your community and prepare fact sheets for reporters or volunteers who will write news releases or assist reporters. The fact sheets could include the health-related consequences of youth alcohol use and infor-

Duplicating this page is illegal. Do not copy this material without written permission from the publisher.

mation on Project Northland. When reporters need someone to interview or background information, respond as thoroughly and quickly as possible. Become a reliable, credible source of information.

■ **Build media relations.**

Learn media deadlines for news releases and other ways to make reporters' and editors' jobs easier. Don't assume that reporters will cover a story just because you sent a news release. Follow up after sending a release. Ask if they have any questions. After receiving positive news coverage, call to express your appreciation or send a thank-you note.

■ **Suggest news stories.**

Take note of which reporters are writing about topics related to youth alcohol use and what topics are current. For example, if the issue of teenage pregnancy is making headlines, suggest a story connecting efforts to reduce underage alcohol use with fewer teenage pregnancies. Consider a new angle to attract the attention of a reporter other than the health or education reporter. For example, the crime reporter might be interested in the connection between vandalism and underage alcohol use, or the business reporter might be interested in what local businesses can do to prevent underage alcohol purchases and how they can benefit from taking this action.

Summary

Your Project Northland communications will inform, inspire, and draw people in. Local media can support your message, so working with them is well worth your while. Connect with people face-to-face, across airwaves, and online to promote your program.

• • •

Duplicating this page is illegal. Do not copy this material without written permission from the publisher.

CHAPTER 10

Program Evaluation

Ongoing evaluation is the key to quality implementation and continued support for your Project Northland program. This chapter will help take the mystery out of conducting your own evaluation, contracting with an external evaluator, or undertaking some combination of both approaches. Equally important to doing evaluation is using the data you gather to make program improvements and communicate your successes. This all begins with developing a strong evaluation plan to go along with your implementation of Project Northland.

▶▶ *What You Will Learn in Chapter 10:*
- Why devote resources to evaluating our program?
- What basic evaluation terms should I know?
- Who should perform the evaluation?
- Gathering evaluation data: when, what, and how?
- How do we report our evaluation results?
- What additional tools may help with Project Northland evaluations?

Why Devote Resources to Evaluating Our Program?

Evaluation is necessary in order to
- highlight successes and areas for improvement
- know what parts of implementation are going well
- know where you may be able to make adjustments that will improve outcomes
- update funders, parents, community members, and teachers
- build enthusiasm
- build the case for program expansion and addressing newly identified needs

Duplicating this page is illegal. Do not copy this material without written permission from the publisher.

These benefits make evaluation essential to long-term success and sustainability—and well worth the time and money required.

 PROGRAM TIP

Are Some of the Staff Uneasy about Evaluation?

It may help to remind people that the purpose of program evaluation is neither testing nor judging. Evaluation is for learning how to make your Project Northland program the best it can be and to help students make healthy decisions regarding underage alcohol use. It can help teachers learn how to improve their instruction, and it can demonstrate the success of their efforts. Used effectively to guide your program, your evaluation findings will give you plenty of reasons to celebrate!

What Basic Evaluation Terms Should I Know?

In developing your Project Northland evaluation plan, you will want to consider two main types of evaluation: outcome evaluation and process evaluation. You will need to establish short-term, intermediate, and long-term goals. Additionally, you will need to identify the baseline measures, indicators, and benchmarks you will use to determine the extent to which you are meeting your goals. In order to do this, you will also need to identify what quantitative and qualitative data you will collect.

 **PROFESSIONAL HIGHLIGHT**

"Fidelity is not perfect, but it's improving, and improved fidelity is correlating to improved results."

DIRECTOR OF PREVENTION PROGRAMS (FLORIDA)

Outcome Evaluation

Outcome evaluation is focused on end results and is sometimes referred to as summative evaluation. For example, it asks whether implementation of Project Northland is meeting or has met its main goals, like reducing underage drinking. Outcome evaluation looks at the impact or changes that result from a program. Some outcomes—like delaying the onset of alcohol use—must be measured over long periods of time to fully determine the effects of the program. Because the kinds of change that you are trying to initiate take time to occur, it is important to establish benchmarks along the way. Behaviors around alcohol use are good examples of areas in which it is important to have short-term, intermediate, and long-term goals, such as reducing rates of

Duplicating this page is illegal. Do not copy this material without written permission from the publisher.

underage drinking during the past thirty days, during the past year, and until youth reach age twenty-one.

 PROGRAM TIP

There are at least two main outcomes you will want to assess for Project Northland:

1. Student-level change: Has the program changed student attitudes and behaviors regarding alcohol use?

2. Community-level change: Has the program decreased the ease or frequency of alcohol access for the community's teens?

Community-led compliance checks are both useful and measurable. See page 141 for information about sample data collection forms.

Process Evaluation

Process evaluation looks at how your program is being implemented and is also referred to as formative evaluation. The value of process evaluation should not be underestimated, especially when replication of an evidence-based program like Project Northland is the goal. As you know, Project Northland is built on many years of research about effective alcohol prevention strategies. Closely following instructions for implementing key program elements is termed "fidelity." The fidelity with which the program is implemented is likely to be related to outcomes. The more completely the Project Northland guidelines are followed in your community, the more likely you are to achieve the same strong results that have been achieved in other communities.

 PROGRAM TIP

It is important to have an understanding of student participation, the level of program implementation in classrooms, and the level of satisfaction that teachers and students have with the program.

Duplicating this page is illegal. Do not copy this material without written permission from the publisher.

Short-Term, Intermediate, and Long-Term Goals

When evaluating what you have accomplished, you will want to discuss your results in terms of activity that can be observed over time. Therefore, you will want to establish short-term, intermediate, and long-term goals as a means for assessing your progress. How these periods are defined depends on your overall time frame. When implementing a program such as Project Northland, you might want to consider at least a three-year horizon. Short-term goals are what you expect to happen over a relatively brief period of time, such as the change that you expect to see during a semester. Intermediate goals can be those changes or events that you expect to occur from year to year. Long-term goals would be those that you plan to meet by the end of the implementation period.

Baseline Measures

In order to evaluate change, you must know where you started. This initial data collection is referred to as your baseline measures. You use baseline measures as comparisons to gauge your program's effectiveness over time. Baseline data is often the same information you collected during your needs assessment—to get a sense of community and student attitudes and behaviors around underage drinking—back when you selected Project Northland to help your community address these concerns. If there are any key pieces you did not collect then, you will want to gather that information before you start the program. Baseline measures need to be collected before any program activities begin.

Indicators

In order to determine whether the project is meeting its goals, you will use indicators. Indicators, sometimes called performance standards or data elements, are the measures or signs that you use to determine if you are progressing toward your goals. They tell, for example, the number of Project Northland sessions taught to students, the number of students who participated in all of the sessions, the degree of teacher satisfaction with the instructional

Duplicating this page is illegal. Do not copy this material without written permission from the publisher.

materials, and parent perceptions about the Project Northland activities done with their children. Indicators link your data with your goals. They are the items of information that indicate the extent to which your program is succeeding

Benchmarks

The specific targets of change, increase, reduction, or satisfaction that you hope to achieve are your benchmarks. You do not want to wait until the end of your implementation period to find out how successful you have been, so it is important to establish benchmarks for what you plan to achieve along the way. If your indicators reach the benchmark levels, then you know that your program is on the right track to yielding positive results. If the indicators show that your benchmarks are not being met, then you need to decide on program implementation changes that are likely to position you for greater success. For example, if the percentage of parents completing homework assignments with their children is lower than what you would like to see, you might host a parent meeting or make phone calls or home visits to encourage greater parent involvement in Project Northland activities.

Quantitative Data

Quantitative data includes information that can be measured as a series of numerical values. It is usually collected in a standardized manner, such as through a survey or from official records. Frequently, indicators are merely counted and used to describe what has taken place, such as the numbers of students being served, students in certain demographic groups (age, ethnicity, native language), the number of teachers who use all key pieces of the program (a fidelity measure), or the number of alcohol-related car crashes over a certain period involving underage drivers. Statistical methods determine the significance of results—that is to say, the likelihood that your results were not purely due to chance. This is often done when comparing data, such as the rate of binge drinking among students participating in Project Northland compared to the rate of their national counterparts.

PROGRAM TIP

If indicators of success reach benchmark levels, then the program is yielding positive results.

Duplicating this page is illegal. Do not copy this material without written permission from the publisher.

131

Qualitative Data

Qualitative data is more experiential information that is used to identify recurrent themes and patterns expressed or demonstrated by the individuals being studied. It is usually collected through interviews, classroom observations, focus groups, photographs, or case studies. A critical aspect is the flexibility respondents have in answering questions. The purpose of qualitative data is to help increase understanding of what is being examined, rather than obtain a precise measurement. This would include data related, for example, to what teachers, students, parents, and other community members have to say about different aspects of the program, what they like or do not like about the curriculum, how they describe the ways in which their attitudes and behaviors have changed as a result of participating in Project Northland, and levels of program participation.

Who Should Perform the Evaluation?

Evaluations done by the program staff or coalition volunteers are generally referred to as internal evaluations. Evaluations done by a college, university, or consultant are generally referred to as external evaluations. There are pros and cons to using one approach or the other. Therefore, an approach that involves a combination of the two, known as participatory evaluation, is gaining in popularity. The chart on page 133 outlines some of the main factors to consider in deciding who should be involved in evaluating your implementation of Project Northland—objectivity, credibility, expertise, usefulness, success, and cost.

While you may have the expertise and time available to perform an internal evaluation of your Project Northland program, some funders may require that you use an external evaluator. Even if it is not required, you might want to consider hiring an evaluation consultant if you have a need for assistance with data collection (for example, in developing surveys and questionnaires, conducting a focus group, or interviewing key informants),

Duplicating this page is illegal. Do not copy this material without written permission from the publisher.

if you need help with the statistical analysis or coding of your data, if the program is under close scrutiny from critics, or if the focus of the evaluation is unclear.

If you decide to hire a consultant, you will still need to allocate time for making sure that the consultant understands how your Project Northland program functions and what information will be most useful for you to get from the evaluation. In selecting an evaluator, you might want to consider which of the program situations in the chart on page 134 best reflects your own situation and the skills you will want your evaluator to possess.

Comparison of Internal and External Evaluation

	INTERNAL EVALUATION	EXTERNAL EVALUATION
Objectivity	Can be perceived as being less objective	Usually perceived as being more objective about the program because of lower level of direct connection with the program
Credibility	Can be seen as less credible due to lack of evaluation expertise	Usually perceived as more credible, provided sufficient time is taken to understand program functioning
Expertise	Skilled and knowledgeable about program functioning	Skilled and knowledgeable about evaluation
Usefulness	May be more useful because of familiarity with the program	May be less useful because of lack of familiarity with the program
Success	May be more successful in getting support from other program staff	May be less successful in getting support from other program staff
Cost	Less expensive	More expensive

Source: CSAP's Western Center for the Application of Prevention Technologies

Duplicating this page is illegal. Do not copy this material without written permission from the publisher.

Choose an Evaluator with the Right Skills

PROGRAM SITUATION	CHALLENGE	EVALUATOR SKILLS TO LOOK FOR
Controversy over the program and how to evaluate it	Facilitating different points of view	• Conflict resolutions skills • Team-building skills • Neutrality and objectivity
Highly visible program	Dealing with publicity, reporting findings in a political environment	• Public presentation skills • Experience with media and politicians • Credible reputation and experience
Flexible, highly dynamic program	Adapting to rapid changes in context, issues, focus	• Tolerance for ambiguity • Flexibility • Skills in qualitative methods • Quick learner
Collaborative program (team effort)	Managing people	• Team-building skills • Ability to focus and direct progress • Experience in participatory evaluation

Source: Adapted from materials by the W.K. Kellogg Foundation and CSAP's Western Center for the Application of Prevention Technologies

Gathering Evaulation Data:
When, What, and How?

Program evaluation is something you must begin to consider from the earliest planning stages of your implementation. Evaluation data feeds into your ongoing needs assessment and resource development activities, thus ensuring the sustainability of your Project Northland program. Your evaluation plan should include information about how frequently you will collect, analyze, and report on various program indicators. An Evaluation Action Plan form is provided on the CD-ROM accompanying this manual. Some indicators, generally parts of your process evaluation, may warrant monthly or quarterly assessments. For example, one of your funding agencies may require regular reports on the number of students served and the number of hours spent delivering Project Northland. Outcome data and some other pieces, such as community readiness surveys and parent focus groups, might only be collected annually or even every other year.

Duplicating this page is illegal. Do not copy this material without written permission from the publisher.

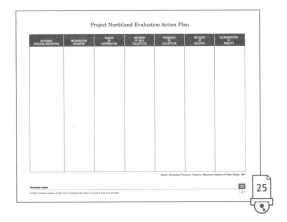

Project Northland Evaluation Action Plan

Government Performance and Results Act (GPRA) Requirements

The Government Performance and Results Act of 1993 (P.L.103-62) requires all federal agencies to set program performance targets and report annually on the degree to which the previous year's targets were met. Congress uses this information to determine funding priorities each year. The performance targets vary by agency and program. Therefore, it is very important that you know what the reporting requirements are if you receive federal funding. GPRA requirements for two programs that often help to implement Project Northland are provided below.

The U.S. Department of Education has established the following three GPRA measures as indicators of success for the Grants to Reduce Alcohol Abuse (GRAA) program:

1. The percentage of grantees whose target students show a measurable decrease in binge drinking

2. The percentage of grantees that show a measurable increase in the percentage of target students who believe that alcohol abuse is harmful to their health

3. The percentage of grantees that show a measurable increase in the percentage of target students who disapprove of alcohol abuse

Duplicating this page is illegal. Do not copy this material without written permission from the publisher.

PROFESSIONAL HIGHLIGHT

"Seventy-five percent of the comparison group students did not use marijuana in the last twelve months, while 90 percent of the eighth-grade Project Northland group reported no use."

WILDER RESEARCH (MINNESOTA)

The Office of National Drug Control Policy (ONDCP) and Substance Abuse and Mental Health Services Administration (SAMHSA) use the following four core measures to meet the GPRA requirements for the Drug Free Communities (DFC) Support Program:

1. Past Thirty-Day Use

   • The percentage of respondents who report using alcohol, tobacco, or marijuana at least *once* in the past thirty days

2. Average Age of Onset

   • The average age that respondents report first trying alcohol, tobacco, or marijuana

3. Perception of Risk

   • The percentage of respondents who report that regular use of alcohol, tobacco, or marijuana has moderate risk or great risk

     – Regular use is defined for alcohol as one or two drinks of an alcoholic beverage (beer, wine, liquor) nearly every day.

     – Regular use is defined for tobacco as one or more packs of cigarettes a day.

     – Regular use for marijuana is not defined.

4. Perception of Parental Disapproval

   • The percentage of respondents who report their parents feel regular use of alcohol is wrong or very wrong

   • The percentage of respondents who report their parents feel *any* use of cigarettes or marijuana is wrong or very wrong

Duplicating this page is illegal. Do not copy this material without written permission from the publisher.

A Guide for Reporting the Four Core Measures Required of Drug Free Communities Support Program Grantees was developed to help DFC grantees accurately collect data on the four core measures. While intended for DFC grantees, this guide may also be useful to you in identifying or developing survey instruments to collect your evaluation data. The guide provides an overview of the questions that will meet the core data measures most commonly used by DFC grantees, questionnaire-specific examples of questions and how to report the data generated by them, and additional resources.

Another resource for collecting this type of information is the Substance Abuse Risk and Protective Factor (SARPF) Student Survey made available by the Center for Substance Abuse Prevention at no cost. Other questionnaires that meet the core measures are the Communities That Care (CTC) Youth Survey and the Pride Risk and Protective Factor Survey. Information about all four surveys described above is available on the CD-ROM.

Comparison Data

Monitoring the Future is an ongoing study of the behaviors, attitudes, and values of American secondary school students, college students, and young adults. The Youth Risk Behavior Surveillance System (YRBSS) also monitors priority health-risk behaviors among youth and young adults. Both of these organizations provide annual national data back to 1991 that can be compared with your local data.

Statewide surveys of adolescent attitudes and behavior related to health, education, and prevention exist in most states. This data is also useful for helping to determine how underage drinking in your community compares with that in other parts of the country. Some existing surveys of this sort are listed on the CD-ROM.

Duplicating this page is illegal. Do not copy this material without written permission from the publisher.

You may also want to compare your outcomes with the results of the original Project Northland study done by the University of Minnesota's Division of Epidemiology & Community Health. Those results showed that, relative to students in the control group,

- Project Northland participants demonstrated reduced levels of alcohol, marijuana, and cigarette use, and they displayed more resilient behaviors.

- Students who participated in Project Northland showed 30 percent lower weekly drinking and 20 percent lower monthly drinking.

- Over time, they engaged in 27 percent lower cigarette use and 27 percent lower alcohol use by the end of eighth grade.

 PROFESSIONAL HIGHLIGHT

Effective Evaluation Informs ROE's Implementation

The director of one ROE's (regional office of education) implementation shares helpful tips for Project Northland evaluation:

We have done our outcome evaluation largely by using the national Pride survey. Pride is one of the few organizations that could also give us both local and national comparative data. They have a large sample drawn from across the United States. It's similar to the Monitoring the Future survey, but does not contain as many questions and can be administered locally. It enabled us to collect the right data related to national indicators to assess Project Northland. We can see how they change from year to year as we use the program. About half of the schools in our area are participating in Project Northland and half are not. This gives us a natural comparison group. Looking at student responses in sixth, eighth, tenth, and twelfth grades has shown tremendous favorable differences on almost all indicators between students who have participated in Project Northland and those who have not.

We also collect a lot of data for our process evaluation, like: How long did it take to deliver all of the sessions, how many sessions were delivered, the length of each session, student attendance, and teacher, parent, and student satisfaction with the program. We pull this data together to look at fidelity issues and what improvements we can make in the program for the next year.

The 2007–2008 school year marked the completion of the seventh three-year implementation cycle for Project Northland in most of the region's participating schools and the fourth three-year cycle in the others. Since 1999, they have had more than 8,910 sixth graders participate in *Slick Tracy,* more than 6,920 seventh graders participate in *Amazing Alternatives,* more than 5,470 eighth graders participate in *Power Lines,* and more than 1,875 high school students complete the program with *Class Action.* The ROE's evaluation clearly demonstrates that progress has been made in reducing underage alcohol use among Project Northland participants.

Duplicating this page is illegal. Do not copy this material without written permission from the publisher.

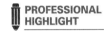

- These students also demonstrated markedly lower drug use by the end of eighth grade.

- Intervention group students who never drank alcohol at the beginning of sixth grade showed 50 percent lower marijuana use and 37 percent lower cigarette use by the end of eighth grade.

- Students whose risk of drinking was lowered by Project Northland also demonstrated less growth of family problems and less likelihood to use both alcohol and drugs than students in the control group.[1]

Implement Project Northland with Fidelity

Since we know that Project Northland has been proven to be effective in a variety of settings, it is desirable to stay true to the Project Northland Fidelity Guidelines on the CD-ROM accompanying this manual. There are key aspects of the original program to which it is crucial to remain faithful in order to ensure the same positive outcomes. As discussed in chapter 3, there are some modifications that might make Project Northland more relevant in your community, like reading the *Amazing Alternatives* scripts aloud rather than listening to the recordings, rerecording the scripts using local voices, or changing details within the scripts to better reflect a favorite pastime of your students. Such variations might enhance the program or make it fit better with your locale.

PROFESSIONAL HIGHLIGHT

"Eighth graders' post-survey score (25.61) is better than the eighth-grade comparison group (32.54), which indicates the Project Northland group as a whole is less influenced by their friends to drink alcohol."

WILDER RESEARCH
(MINNESOTA)

Duplicating this page is illegal. Do not copy this material without written permission from the publisher.

139

Acceptable modifications have been introduced in chapter 3 and are explained in the Project Northland Fidelity Guidelines. Generally, these are minor adaptations like changing names and settings within the materials to more closely match your students' social environment. Components may be added to enhance the Project Northland activities, such as including Poster Fair judges to involve prominent community members or sponsoring a billboard or radio public service announcement contest for participating students. The timing of lesson delivery may be adapted. For example, lessons could be taught every other week. However, do give families at least one week between lessons to complete Home Team activities with their children. Adaptations may also be made to accommodate specific student needs. For example, low-proficiency readers—including Peer Leaders—may choose someone to help them read aloud.

As a part of your process evaluation, it is critically important that you keep track of all changes you make to Project Northland so that you can determine whether or not they have an impact on your program outcomes. A sample log is provided on the CD-ROM accompanying this manual. This is especially important if multiple teachers will be implementing the program. Ideally, you should begin to answer the following questions about any adaptations to the program before you make changes:

Duplicating this page is illegal. Do not copy this material without written permission from the publisher.

- How did you decide the program needed to be adapted? What evidence did you have to support this assessment?

- Was the process intentional? Unintentional? Both? How did you go about making this decision?

- How do you know your adaptation was congruent with the Project Northland Fidelity Guidelines?

- What did you do to modify the program?

- Did it seem to work? What evidence do you have to support your assessment?

Include Multiple Perspectives

It is important to get input from a variety of perspectives to accurately assess how implementation is going. You will want to hear what teachers, students, parents, and other community members have to say. This information can be gathered using a number of different methods, such as surveys, interviews, and focus groups. The CD-ROM includes several evaluation tools you can copy and use for this purpose:

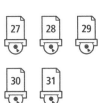

- student surveys and protocol

- parent survey

- alcohol purchase protocol and form

- curriculum process evaluation

Assess Changes in Community Readiness

Expect that your community's level of readiness to make prevention of underage alcohol use a priority will influence your program results. Project Northland has a built-in expectation of support from local communities. This distinguishes the program from other prevention efforts both by making it uniquely effective and by providing many opportunities for you to partner with community organizations. Be sure that your evaluation plan includes indicators related to your community mobilization efforts. You will want to look at how, and to what extent, parent and community attitudes and behaviors are changing because of the program. Try to identify one or more partner organizations—perhaps a local

Duplicating this page is illegal. Do not copy this material without written permission from the publisher.

newspaper—with whom you might conduct an annual community survey.

Use Available Data

You do not have to do all the data collection by yourself. There are many other entities that may be collecting relevant data and measures. Working with your local law enforcement, social services, and public health agencies will help you to gain access to information that they are required to submit to the state or federal governments. These sources may be able to provide you with information about the number of traffic accidents, sexual assaults, teen pregnancies, and other health and safety incidents that have been associated with underage drinking. You can then analyze any changes since implementing Project Northland in your community.

 PROGRAM TIP

Free Web Site Can Help with Data Collection

SurveyMonkey.com may be just what you need to collect information from individuals who have access to the Internet. Putting your survey online may greatly enhance the likelihood that you get more and quicker responses. SurveyMonkey is available free of charge for smaller projects. It is very easy to use and allows you to export your data to analyze and store it. You can also print reports from the Web site. For more information, visit SurveyMonkey online at http://www.surveymonkey .com.

Be Creative

You can include photographs and videos of students and teachers at work, people interacting at Poster Fairs, and other program highlights in your evaluation documentation to provide an excellent record of the activities. Keep a record of quotes and stories from teachers, students, parents, and other community members telling in their own words what they learned, what surprised them, what they liked best, what it was like to be involved with Project Northland, or how they feel Project Northland changed them or the community. This information can also be included in your evaluation reports and presentations to make them more lively and interesting.

Duplicating this page is illegal. Do not copy this material without written permission from the publisher.

How Do We Report Our Evaluation Results?

Evaluations, like any research, are only useful if people receive, read, and understand the results. Excellent, clear writing is important. Furthermore, an evaluation report will ideally go beyond reporting results, though doing so is, of course, crucial. It involves more than merely stating what you did. It requires careful reflection on and analysis of the information you collected. Good evaluation is proactive. It looks forward as much as back, giving direction to your future activities. By offering clear recommendations that people can follow, you can keep receiving good results and/or improvements in the program.

Whether you can afford to hire a communication specialist or will need to write the reports yourself, it is important to know your various audiences and what you want to communicate to them. Best practice suggests that you prepare multiple versions of your report to best inform these various audiences rather than try to do everything within one report. Few individuals will read your entire comprehensive evaluation report.

Before you begin writing, you might want to bring together a small group of people who have been involved with implementing Project Northland to jointly reflect on the data you have collected and to share ways of interpreting it. It is useful to keep in mind why you are doing the evaluation in the first place: to review what you have done, to see what progress or impact you have made, to find out how participants feel about Project Northland, to learn what you can improve for the future, and to build enthusiasm and support for the program among the various stakeholders.

Review everything carefully and create an executive summary no longer than two to five pages that summarizes the following:

- what you did in the program
- how you evaluated
- what your key findings are in relation to main outcome indicators and process information
- lessons learned
- recommendations for the future

Duplicating this page is illegal. Do not copy this material without written permission from the publisher.

Next, you will need to break it down into specialized pieces geared to what is relevant to each audience, such as ways to improve classroom instruction, ideas for strengthening parent involvement, and strategies for expanding community collaborations. Funders may need different information than parents, teachers, legislators, or other community members do.

Consider these tips for strengthening your reports:

■ **Write a brief introduction** describing your Project Northland program, why your community chose Project Northland, and what your goals or targets were for the period you will be covering in the report.

■ **Explain the kinds of data you gathered** for the outcome and process components, as well as how you gathered that data.

■ **Lay out your evaluation findings** in these two main categories:

• Outcomes and indicators that show changes in student and parent behavior related to underage drinking. You will want to be sure to give baseline and/or statewide or national information for comparison, where appropriate and available.

• Process data, including such information as the numbers of students reached, demographics of students reached, number of lessons taught, number of events held, and also information about experiences and satisfaction gathered from any case studies, interviews, focus groups, or observations completed.

■ **Discuss the amount of money, time, and other resources** that were put into the program. Were the resources adequate? Did you have too much of some things and not enough of others?

■ **Analyze your results:** Were you surprised, gratified, pleased, displeased? What factors do you think contributed most to the results?

Duplicating this page is illegal. Do not copy this material without written permission from the publisher.

- **Describe the lessons learned** from the work as a whole, as well as from specific activities.

- **Make recommendations** for the future, specifying who should do what.

- **Describe how you can keep improving** Project Northland and gaining positive results in order to create a shared vision of where the community should be heading.

When you evaluate well, you will be able to write high-quality evaluation reports. The recommendations you make in them will help Project Northland to better serve your community in several ways:

- **They will help you gain more funding.** The number one thing that funders want to see is how well you are achieving your goals and how clear you are about what you need to improve or enhance to meet or exceed your goals. Your evaluation report will tell funding agencies what you have done and how you have done it. It will show that you have reflected on your work and that you have a game plan for how to proceed.

- **They will help you improve your work.** Continuous improvement should be a goal of every program, no matter how successful from the start.

- **They will help you keep your community, volunteers, teachers, and support people motivated.** Nothing says "this is a well-run program that is worth doing" like good results and a plan to do even better.

- **They will help you and the community recognize and celebrate your accomplishments,** even as you move on to accomplish more.

Duplicating this page is illegal. Do not copy this material without written permission from the publisher.

145

What Additional Tools May Help with Project Northland Evaluations?

Links and publications that you may find useful in planning your program evaluation may be found on the CD-ROM accompanying this manual.

Summary

Evaluation is essential to a sustainable program. It helps implementers review and articulate progress and accomplishments, learn from experiences, and continually improve. It helps pinpoint, trumpet, and reproduce your successes.

•   •   •

Duplicating this page is illegal. Do not copy this material without written permission from the publisher.

Sustaining Your Program

Sustainability is a process as well as a capacity that aims to generate long-term support for the implementation and growth of your Project Northland program. Although this chapter comes last, do read it before program implementation, as your initial steps may have far-reaching effects. Sustainability considerations must be included at every stage of program implementation. This will help your program continue effectively long after the initial grant period has ended.

▶▶ *What You Will Learn in Chapter 11:*

- How do implementers sustain their programs over the long term?

- What does self-sustaining Project Northland implementation look like?

- What sustainability tips do experts recommend?

How Do Implementers Sustain Their Programs Over the Long Term?

Sustainability is crafted throughout program development to allow program renewal over time. As you work through one program cycle, your efforts build momentum for future cycles. Here are examples of what you can do to build sustainability at each stage of Project Northland implementation:

Pre-implementation

- Think ahead toward full implementation of Project Northland in your community. What will it look like? Who will be important and necessary for you to involve?

- Plan ahead to request funding for several years in order to get Project Northland fully implemented.

- Keep track of any funding sources that reject your proposals or are not

Duplicating this page is illegal. Do not copy this material without written permission from the publisher.

147

a good fit now. In the future, you may reconnect with these organizations, and they may decide to support your program.

- Keep both printed and electronic copies of all your funding applications and information, so they are available when you apply for future funding.

- Start building relationships with funders now.

- Find champions within schools, community agencies, school districts, local and state government, and national agencies.

- Build links with local businesses.

- Build connections with appropriate parent organizations (PTO/PTA, school board) and with individual parents, especially those who want to work with and champion the program. Attend school board meetings when appropriate.

- Build connections with local, regional, and state groups dedicated to common safety and sobriety goals.

- As soon as you know that the program is going to be implemented in at least one grade, start publicizing it.

Implementation

- During implementation, you are always in the pre-implementation stage of your next implementation cycle, so continue with the suggestions outlined above.

- Keep track of materials and notes on what you learn from launching the program, training teachers, working with teachers and peer leaders, working with government agencies and other entities (hospitals, bar associations, public safety and health offices), and working with community members.

- Keep good records of who donated what. People who donate time, goods, services, or money one time are likely to donate again if they see a benefit for themselves (good publicity, appreciation, greater safety for their family members, the feeling of being part of something important) and the

Duplicating this page is illegal. Do not copy this material without written permission from the publisher.

community (good results). Also, you may be able to encourage new businesses to participate at a later stage, perhaps even at a higher level, if they find out that their competitors have participated and received publicity as a result.

- Thank and appreciate generously. It will never hurt, and always help, if you thank people with cards, public acknowledgment, thank-you events, e-mails, sponsor appreciation events, or rewards such as coupons or free placards announcing that they are Project Northland sponsors.

- Provide continuous communication and opportunities to participate. Let people know through a Web site, a column in the local paper, direct e-mails, and any other means available what Project Northland is, why it is a strong program, what the statistics are involving alcohol use by youth, what is happening in your local programs, and how people can become involved.

- Support teachers as much as possible to make the program effective.

- Keep track of work accomplished, problems encountered (and how they are addressed), program outputs (how many people are served), and program outcomes. It will be difficult or impossible to gather all this information at the end. Remember, evaluation work needs to be ongoing.

- Utilize the publicity guidelines in chapter 9.

Post-implementation

- Follow the sustainability guidelines for pre-implementation and implementation. Successful long-term work is a series of cycles. Various stages of the work are continuing and blending simultaneously.

- Evaluate well and thoroughly.

- Publicize your results.

- Celebrate results, thank people, announce new goals, and mobilize people to keep the momentum going.

PROGRAM TIP

You may find these resources particularly helpful for building sustainability.

Duplicating this page is illegal. Do not copy this material without written permission from the publisher.

- Use what you have learned, whom you have worked with, and what you have achieved to gain new supporters and continuing support.

What Does Self-Sustaining Project Northland Implementation Look Like?

When you start Project Northland, you are working to gain a critical mass of knowledge, interest, and participation. There will be bugs to work out of the system, networking to do, a public to educate, and new curricula for your schools. Over time, the program will grow familiar, run more smoothly, become known, include more supporters, and become established in the schools and communities. Here is what your program could look like a few years into implementation:

Students

Each time the curriculum cycle repeats, new generations of students anticipate their chance to do the exciting projects their older siblings and peers have experienced. Students look forward to participating in the *Slick Tracy* Home Team program, presenting the *Slick Tracy* Poster Fair, planning *Amazing Alternatives* events, investigating community issues for *Power Lines,* and presenting their cases during *Class Action.*

Parents

Educating students through Project Northland means educating parents. As children move through these alcohol-use prevention programs, parents learn more about how to keep their children safe from alcohol and other drugs, the importance of communicating a no-use message about underage alcohol use, how to support their teens' development, and how to communicate about important issues as a family.

Duplicating this page is illegal. Do not copy this material without written permission from the publisher.

Teachers

The more teachers experience Project Northland, the more skill, wisdom, and insight they will bring to the program. The program becomes a familiar part of the academic year. People no longer think of it as an "extra" because it has become an integral part of the school culture.

Community

Project Northland has grown roots so deep into the community and yielded fruit so life-sustaining that no one would dream of cutting it down. Over time, the program has become a community centerpiece well established in the local landscape.

What Sustainability Tips Do Experts Recommend?

Project Northland has met sustainability challenges for more than eighteen years. This advice is collected from experienced implementers:

- Find community volunteers who can pick up pieces of it over time; work your way out of a job as a program coordinator by replacing yourself with others who are trained and willing to be available. So, the parent-teacher organization/association (PTO/PTA) might find a good organizer for the sixth-grade Poster Fair and then one for the event nights for other curricula. Build it in to PTO/PTA parent duties over time so that the work is embedded in the school culture and can be continued at minimal expense.

- Show people—first from results of comparable communities elsewhere and then, very important, from results in your own community—that Project Northland works.

- Funding, teacher turnover, and momentum are often challenges to sustainability.

Duplicating this page is illegal. Do not copy this material without written permission from the publisher.

Funding Challenges

These ideas can help your program stay financially fit:

- From the earliest planning stages, realistically anticipate project expenses and think through how you will sustain Project Northland after the initial grant period ends. Build sustainability into your budgets and grant applications.

- Early in program implementation, establish partnerships with local funding sources (city, county, tribal, and so on) to help fund Project Northland as part of public initiatives. Information about public safety funds and other funds available at the county level is publicly available and may be accessed online or through government offices.

- Conduct program evaluation to document your program's impact. It makes a difference when you have collected data to prove your program's effectiveness.

- When you can, cut back on program costs. For example, you might find less expensive incentives to reward *Slick Tracy* participation.

- Continually seek additional sources of financial support. For example, local auto insurance agents may sponsor *Slick Tracy* by donating funds for the comic books.

Teacher Turnover Challenges

Meet the challenge of teacher turnover and its resulting lack of trained program staff with these tips:

- When you schedule trainings with Hazelden, always train as many people as possible, so that there are others to step in to teach or assist in teaching.

- Provide annual training for all teachers new to Project Northland.

- After professional training from Hazelden, some training may be provided by a skilled and experienced program coordinator.

Duplicating this page is illegal. Do not copy this material without written permission from the publisher.

Momentum Challenges

It is important to keep the program fresh year after year. Here are solutions for maintaining interest, involvement, and enthusiasm over the long haul:

- Envision your program broadly enough from the start. Project Northland is a program for long-term community-wide change.

- Network with the potential stakeholders. Build relationships with them. Keep in touch to let them know what is happening with Project Northland and share results.

- Keep the program in the news and in the public eye. For example, display the *Slick Tracy* posters in shopping centers or hospitals, or present the *Class Action* mock trials to parents and community members.

- Communities that lower the number of alcohol-related problems among people under twenty-one eventually realize a cost savings; over time, it may become possible to return some of that savings to the community. Work with the city or state to set communitywide goals and incentives that matter to people.

Summary

Your Project Northland program, and its impact, will develop over time. It will serve you well to begin your efforts with the end goals in mind and build sustainably at every step along the way. Remember, the goal—both worthwhile and attainable—is to create an effective prevention program that will benefit your students and your community for many years to come.

. . .

Duplicating this page is illegal. Do not copy this material without written permission from the publisher.

153

Resources

There are many wonderful organizations you can learn from and use as resources. The four listed here may be especially helpful when getting started with Project Northland. A more comprehensive resource list is included on the CD-ROM.

Community Anti-Drug Coalitions of America (CADCA)

http://www.cadca.org

CADCA's mission is to "strengthen the capacity of community coalitions to create and maintain safe, healthy, and drug-free communities."

Particularly useful parts of the CADCA Web site include the following:

- the FAQ on training provided by CADCA:
  http://www.cadca.org/CoalitionResources/faq

- the section on evaluation and research: http://www. coalitioninstitute .org/Evaluation-Research/EvaluationResearchHome.asp

- the practical, helpful Strategic Prevention Framework and related materials:
  http://www.coalitioninstitute.org/SPF_Elements/SPFElementsHome.asp

Substance Abuse and Mental Health Services Administration of the U.S. Department of Health and Human Services (SAMHSA)

http://www.samhsa.gov

SAMHSA has "established a clear vision for its work—a life in the community for everyone. To realize this vision, the Agency has sharply focused its mission on building resilience and facilitating recovery for people with or at risk for mental or substance use disorders. SAMHSA is gearing all of its resources— programs, policies, and grants—toward that outcome."

Particularly useful parts of the SAMHSA Web site include the following:

- grants offered by SAMHSA:
  http://www.samhsa.gov/grants/2009/fy2009.aspx

- a treasure trove of up-to-date data: http://www.oas.samhsa.gov

Duplicating this page is illegal. Do not copy this material without written permission from the publisher.

- an extensive list of reports and other publications:
  http://www.oas.samhsa.gov/oasftp.cfm#Pubs

Communities That Care (CTC)

http://ncadi.samhsa.gov/features/ctc/resources.aspx

Communities That Care, part of SAMHSA's National Clearinghouse for
Alcohol and Drug Information, is a system developed by J. David Hawkins and
Richard F. Catalano that "empowers communities to use advances from prevention science to guide their prevention efforts." Communities That Care has
many useful materials available as links or for a fee.

National Institute on Alcohol Abuse and Alcoholism (NIAAA)

http://www.niaaa.nih.gov

NIAAA's publications, resources, and FAQs for the general public are
particularly useful.

Duplicating this page is illegal. Do not copy this material without written permission from the publisher.

PROGRAM GUIDE CD-ROM MATERIALS

CHAPTER	FILE NO.	DOCUMENT
Chapter 1: **Welcome to** **Project Northland!**	1	*Program Guide* CD-ROM Materials
	2	Research Papers Related to Project Northland
	3	Project Northland Fidelity Tools
		3a. Project Northland Fidelity Guidelines
		3b. Classroom Checklists
		3c. Fidelity Checklist for Project Northland Communities
	4	Introduction to Underage Alcohol Issues
	5	Project Northland Scope and Sequence
	18	Session Descriptions and Preparation
		18a. *Slick Tracy* Session Descriptions and Preparation
		18b. *Amazing Alternatives* Session Descriptions and Preparation
		18c. *Power Lines* Session Descriptions and Preparation
	6	Meeting National Academic Standards with Project Northland
Chapter 2: **Responsibilities** **of the** **Project Northland** **Coordinator**	7	Resources and Links by Topic
	8	Project Northland Implementation Worksheet
	12f	Sample Logic Models
Chapter 3: **Bringing Project** **Northland to** **Your Community**	9	Cultural Competence Guidelines
	7	Resources and Links by Topic
	10	Community Assessment Worksheet
	3a	Project Northland Fidelity Guidelines
	11	Fact Sheets
		11a. How Does Project Northland Benefit Businesses?
		11b. How Does Project Northland Benefit Law Enforcement?
		11c. How Does Project Northland Benefit Communities?
		11d. How Does Project Northland Benefit Businesses That Serve Alcohol?
		11e. Drinking and Driving
		11f. Kids and Alcohol
		11g. The Importance of Early Alcohol-Use Prevention
		11h. Risks of Underage Alcohol Use among U.S. Youth
		11i. What Is Project Northland?
		11j. Family Involvement Is Key

continued on next page

Duplicating this material for personal or group use is permissible.

PROGRAM GUIDE CD-ROM MATERIALS		
CHAPTER	**FILE NO.**	**DOCUMENT**
Chapter 4: **Funding Your** **Program**	12	Project Northland Funding Toolkit
		12a. Welcome to the Project Northland Funding Toolkit!
		12b. Guide to Successful Grant Writing
		12c. Grant Application Template
		12d. Sample Letter Requesting a Letter of Commitment
		12e. Sample Letter of Commitment
		12f. Sample Logic Models
		12g. Sample Grant Application Transmittal Letter
	13	Hazelden Information
	7	Resources and Links by Topic
	10	Community Assessment Worksheet
	11	Fact Sheets
		11a. How Does Project Northland Benefit Businesses?
		11b. How Does Project Northland Benefit Law Enforcement?
		11c. How Does Project Northland Benefit Communities?
		11d. How Does Project Northland Benefit Businesses That Serve Alcohol?
		11e. Drinking and Driving
		11f. Kids and Alcohol
		11g. The Importance of Early Alcohol-Use Prevention
		11h. Risks of Underage Alcohol Use among U.S. Youth
		11i. What Is Project Northland?
		11j. Family Involvement Is Key
	2	Research Papers Related to Project Northland
Chapter 5: **Implementing** **Project Northland**	8	Project Northland Implementation Worksheet
	13	Hazelden Information
	14	Project Northland Training Materials
		14a. Project Northland Training Worksheet
		14b. Project Northland Training Sign-In Sheet
	11	Fact Sheets
		11a. How Does Project Northland Benefit Businesses?
		11b. How Does Project Northland Benefit Law Enforcement?
		11c. How Does Project Northland Benefit Communities?
		11d. How Does Project Northland Benefit Businesses That Serve Alcohol?
		11e. Drinking and Driving
		11f. Kids and Alcohol
		11g. The Importance of Early Alcohol-Use Prevention
		11h. Risks of Underage Alcohol Use among U.S. Youth
		11i. What Is Project Northland?
		11j. Family Involvement Is Key

continued on next page

Duplicating this material for personal or group use is permissible.

CHAPTER	FILE NO.	DOCUMENT
Chapter 5: **Implementing** **Project Northland** *(continued)*	3b	Classroom Checklists
	15	Project Northland Community Launch Party
		15a. Project Northland Community Launch Party Worksheet
		15b. Project Northland Community Launch Party Sign-In Sheet
	16	Volunteer Sign-Up Sheets
Chapter 6: **Supporting Teachers** **and Learners**	3b	Classroom Checklists
	17	Peer Leader Training Resources
		17a. Introduction to Peer Leader Training Resources
		17b. *Slick Tracy* Peer Leader Training
		17c. *Slick Tracy* Planning Page for Peer Leader Training
		17d. *Amazing Alternatives* Planning Page for Peer Leader Training
		17e. Helpful Hints for Peer Leaders
		17f. Troubleshooting for Peer Leaders
		17g. Sample from the *Slick Tracy* Peer Leader Manual
		17h. Sample from the *Amazing Alternatives* Peer Leader Manual
		17i. *Slick Tracy* Peer Leader Training Certificate
		17j. *Amazing Alternatives* Peer Leader Training Certificate
		17k. *Power Lines* Helpful Hints for Shared Leadership
		17l. *Class Action* Helpful Hints for Shared Leadership
	18	Session Descriptions and Preparation
		18a. *Slick Tracy* Session Descriptions and Preparation
		18b. *Amazing Alternatives* Session Descriptions and Preparation
		18c. *Power Lines* Session Descriptions and Preparation
	19	Project Northland Wallet Safety Card
	20	*Slick Tracy* Poster Fair Excerpts
		20a. The *Slick Tracy* Poster Fair
		20b. *Slick Tracy* Poster Fair Projects Annotated List
	21	Information About *Amazing Alternatives* Activities
		21a. Starting a Student Activity Group
		21b. Hosting an *Amazing Alternatives* Fun Night
	22	Power Lines Excerpts
		22a. The *Power Lines* Community Projects
		22b. *Power Lines* Project-Specific Resources
Chapter 7: **Family Involvement**	16	Volunteer Sign-Up Sheets
	11	Fact Sheets
		11a. How Does Project Northland Benefit Businesses?
		11b. How Does Project Northland Benefit Law Enforcement?

continued on next page

Duplicating this material for personal or group use is permissible.

PROGRAM GUIDE CD-ROM MATERIALS		
CHAPTER	**FILE NO.**	**DOCUMENT**
Chapter 7: **Family Involvement** *(continued)*		11c. How Does Project Northland Benefit Communities?
		11d. How Does Project Northland Benefit Businesses That Serve Alcohol?
		11e. Drinking and Driving
		11f. Kids and Alcohol
		11g. The Importance of Early Alcohol-Use Prevention
		11h. Risks of Underage Alcohol Use among U.S. Youth
		11i. What Is Project Northland?
		11j. Family Involvement Is Key
	24a	Announcements and Flyers
Chapter 8: **Community Mobilization**	7	Resources and Links by Topic
	31	Sample Alcohol Purchase/Compliance Check
	21	Information About *Amazing Alternatives* Activities
		21a. Starting a Student Activity Group
		21b. Hosting an *Amazing Alternatives* Fun Night
	23	Gold Card Rewards
		23a. About Gold Card Rewards
		23b. Sample Gold Card Contracts
		23c. Sample Community Service Report
		23d. Sample Letter Requesting Sponsorship from a Business
		23e. Sample Gold Card Sponsorship Form
Chapter 9: **Promoting Your Program**	24	Project Northland Promotional Toolkit
		24a. Announcements and Flyers
		24b. Media Releases
		24c. How to Write a Media Release
	11	Fact Sheets
		11a. How Does Project Northland Benefit Businesses?
		11b. How Does Project Northland Benefit Law Enforcement?
		11c. How Does Project Northland Benefit Communities?
		11d. How Does Project Northland Benefit Businesses That Serve Alcohol?
		11e. Drinking and Driving
		11f. Kids and Alcohol
		11g. The Importance of Early Alcohol-Use Prevention
		11h. Risks of Underage Alcohol Use among U.S. Youth
		11i. What Is Project Northland?
		11j. Family Involvement Is Key

continued on next page

Duplicating this material for personal or group use is permissible.

PROGRAM GUIDE CD-ROM MATERIALS		
CHAPTER	**FILE NO.**	**DOCUMENT**
Chapter 10: **Program Evaluation**	25	Project Northland Evaluation Action Plan
	7	Resources and Links by Topic
	3a	Project Northland Fidelity Guidelines
	26	Project Northland Program Modification Log
	27	Sample Survey of Student Behaviors and Attitudes
	28	Sample Student Satisfaction Survey
	29	Curriculum Process Evaluation
	30	Sample Parent Survey
	31	Sample Alcohol Purchase/Compliance Check
Chapter 11: **Sustaining** **Your Program**	7	Resources and Links by Topic
	10	Community Assessment Worksheet
	13	Hazelden Information

Chapter 1: Welcome to Project Northland!

1. C. L. Williams, C. L. Perry, B. Dudovitz, S. Veblen-Mortenson, P. S. Anstine, K. A. Komro, and T. L. Toomey, "A Home-Based Prevention Program for Sixth Grade Alcohol Use: Results from Project Northland," *Journal of Primary Prevention* 16, no. 2 (1995): 125–47; K. A. Komro, C. L. Perry, D. Murray, S. Veblen-Mortenson, C. L. Williams, and P. Anstine, "Peer-Planned Social Activities for Preventing Alcohol Use Among Adolescents," *Journal of School Health* 66, no. 9 (1996): 328–34; C. L. Perry, C. L. Williams, S. Veblen-Mortenson, T. Toomey, K. Komro, P. S. Anstine, P. McGovern, J. R. Finnegan, J. L. Forster, A. C. Wagenaar, and M. Wolfson, "Outcomes of a Community-wide Alcohol Use Prevention Program during Early Adolescence: Project Northland," *American Journal of Public Health* 86, no. 7 (1996): 956–65; T. L. Toomey, C. L. Williams, C. L. Perry, D. M. Murray, B. Dudovitz, and S. Veblen-Mortenson, "An Alcohol Primary Prevention Program for Parents of 7th Graders: The Amazing Alternatives! Home Program," *Journal of Child & Adolescent Substance Abuse* 5, no. 4 (1996): 35–53; C. L. Perry and C. L. Williams, "Project Northland: Outcomes of a Community-wide Adolescent Alcohol Use Prevention Trial," *The Prevention Researcher* 5, no. 2 (1998): 8–12; C. L. Williams and C. L. Perry, "Design and Implementation of Parent Programs for a Community-wide Adolescent Alcohol Use Prevention Program," *Journal of Prevention and Intervention in the Community* 17, no. 2 (1998): 65–80; C. L. Williams and C. L. Perry, "Lessons from Project Northland: Preventing Alcohol Problems during Adolescence," *Alcohol Health & Research World* 22, no.2 (1998): 107–16; S. Veblen-Mortenson, C. E. Rissel, C. L. Perry, M. Wolfson, J. R. Finnegan, and J. Forster, "Lessons Learned from Project Northland: Community Organization in Rural Communities," in *Health Promotion at the Community Level,* 2nd ed., ed. Neil Bracht (Thousand Oaks, CA: Sage Publications, 1999): 105–17; C. L. Williams, C. L. Perry, K. Farbakhsh, and S. Veblen-Mortenson, "Project Northland: Comprehensive Alcohol Use Prevention for Young Adolescents, Their Parents, Schools, Peers, and Communities," *Journal of Studies on Alcohol* S13 (1999): 112–24; K. A. Komro, C. L. Perry, C. L. Williams, M. H. Stigler, K. Farbakhsh, and S. Veblen-Mortenson, "How Did Project Northland Reduce Alcohol Use among Young Adolescents? Analysis of Mediating Variables," *Health Education Research: Theory & Practice* 16, no. 1 (2001): 59–70; C. L. Perry, K. A. Komro, R. M. Jones, K. A. Munson, C. L. Williams, and L. Jason, "The Measurement of Wisdom and Its Relationship to Adolescent Behavior," *Journal of Child and Adolescent Substance Abuse* 12, no. 1 (2002): 45–63; C. L. Perry, C. L. Williams, K. A. Komro, and S. Veblen-Mortenson, "Community Action to Reduce High School Adolescent Alcohol Use," *The Prevention Researcher* 9, no. 3 (2002): 12–15; C. L. Perry, C. L. Williams, K. A. Komro, S. Veblen-Mortenson, M. H. Stigler, K. A. Munson, K. Farbakhsh, R. M. Jones, and J. L. Forster, "Project Northland: Long-Term Outcomes of Community Action to Reduce Adolescent Alcohol Use," *Health Education Research* 17, no. 1 (2002): 117–32; C. L. Perry, S. Lee, M. H. Stigler, K. Farbakhsh, K. A. Komro, A. H. Gewirtz, and C. L. Williams, "The Impact of Project Northland on Selected MMPI-A Problem Behavior Scales," *Journal of Primary Prevention* 28 (2007): 449–65.

Duplicating this page is illegal. Do not copy this material without written permission from the publisher.

2. Perry et al., "Outcomes of a Community-wide Alcohol Use Prevention Program"; Perry and Williams, "Project Northland: Outcomes."

3. R. J. Bonnie and M. E. O'Connell, *Reducing and Preventing Underage Drinking: A Collective Responsibility* (Washington, DC: National Academies of Science, 2004), 196.

4. Komro et al., "How Did Project Northland Reduce Alcohol Use?"; Perry et al., "Outcomes of a Community-wide Alcohol Use Prevention Program"; Perry and Williams, "Project Northland: Outcomes"; Perry et al., "The Impact of Project Northland."

5. Perry et al., "Outcomes of a Community-wide Alcohol Use Prevention Program"; Perry and Williams, "Project Northland: Outcomes."

6. Perry et al., "The Impact of Project Northland."

7. K. A. Komro, C. L. Perry, S. Veblen-Mortenson, K. Farbakhsh, T. L. Toomey, M. H. Stigler, R. Jones-Webb, K. Kugler, K. E. Pasch, and C. L. Williams, "Outcomes from a Randomized Controlled Trial of a Multi-component Alcohol Use Preventive Intervention for Urban Youth: Project Northland Chicago," *Addiction* 103 (2008): 606–18.

8. L. D. Johnston, P. M. O'Malley, J. G. Bachman, and J. E. Schulenberg, "Monitoring the Future National Survey Results on Drug Use, 1975–2007: Volume I, Secondary School Students," NIH Publication no. 08-6418A (Bethesda, MD: National Institute on Drug Abuse, 2008).

9. R. Kosterman, J. D. Hawkins, J. Guo, R. F. Catalano, and R. D. Abbott, "The Dynamics of Alcohol and Marijuana Initiation: Patterns and Predictors of First Use in Adolescence," *American Journal of Public Health* 90, no. 3 (2000): 360–66; National Center for Chronic Disease Prevention and Health Promotion, "YRBSS Youth Online: Comprehensive Results," http://www.cdc.gov/ HealthyYouth/yrbs (retrieved September 12, 2008).

10. National Center for Chronic Disease Prevention and Health Promotion, "YRBSS Youth Online."

11. Johnston et al., "Monitoring the Future."

12. Ibid.

13. B. F. Grant and D. A. Dawson, "Age of Onset of Drug Use and Its Association with DSM-IV Drug Abuse and Dependence: Results from the National Longitudinal Alcohol Epidemiologic Survey," *Journal of Substance Abuse* 10, no. 2 (1998): 163–73; B. F. Grant, F. S. Stinson, and T. Harford, "Age at Onset of Alcohol Use and DSM-IV Alcohol Abuse and Dependence: A 12-Year Follow-Up," *Journal of Substance Abuse* 13 (2001): 493–504; E. Gruber, R. J. DiClemente, M. Anderson, and M. Lodico, "Early Drinking Onset and Its Association with Alcohol Use and Problem Behavior in Late Adolescence," *Preventive Medicine* 25, no. 3 (1996): 293–300; R. Hingson, T. Heeren, S. Levenson, A. Jamanka, and R. Voas, "Age of Drinking Onset, Driving after Drinking, and Involvement in Alcohol Related Motor-Vehicle Crashes," *Accident Analysis and Prevention* 34, no. 1 (2002): 85–92; R. Hingson, T. Heeren, R. Zakocs, M. Winter, and H. Wechsler, "Age of First Intoxication, Heavy Drinking, Driving after Drinking, and Risk of Unintentional Injury among U.S. College Students," *Journal of Studies on Alcohol* 64, no. 1 (2003): 23–31; R. Hingson, T. Heeren, and R. Zakocs, "Age of Drinking Onset and Involvement in Physical Fights after Drinking," *Pediatrics* 108, no. 4 (2001): 872–77; R. Hingson, T. Heeren, M. R. Winter, and H. Wechsler, "Early Age of First Drunkenness as a Factor in College Students' Unplanned and Unprotected Sex Attributable to Drinking," *Pediatrics* 111, no. 1 (2003): 34–41; R. W. Hingson, T. Heeren, and M. R. Winter, "Age at Drinking Onset and Alcohol Dependence—Age at Onset, Duration, and Severity," *Archives of Pediatrics & Adolescent Medicine* 160, no. 7 (2006): 739–46.

Duplicating this page is illegal. Do not copy this material without written permission from the publisher.

14. S. Peele, *Addiction-Proof Your Child* (New York: Random House/Three Rivers Press, 2007).

15. Perry et al., "Outcomes of a Community-wide Alcohol Use Prevention Program"; Perry and Williams, "Project Northland: Outcomes."

16. C. L. Odgers, A. Caspi, D. S. Nagin, A. R. Piquero, W. S. Slutske, B. J. Milne, N. Dickson, R. Poulton, and T. E. Moffitt, "Is It Important to Prevent Early Exposure to Drugs and Alcohol Among Adolescents?" *Psychological Science* 19, no. 10 (2008): 1037–44.

17. S. Hiller-Sturmhöfel and H. S. Swartzwelder, "Alcohol's Effects on the Adolescent Brain: What Can Be Learned from Animal Models," *Alcohol Research & Health* 28, no. 4 (2004/2005): 213–21; B. Lopez, S. J. Schwartz, G. Prado, A. E. Campo, and H. Pantin, "Adolescent Neurological Development and Its Implications for Adolescent Substance Abuse Prevention," *Journal of Primary Prevention* 29 (2008): 5–35; B. Luna and J. A. Sweeney, "The Emergence of Collaborative Brain Function," *Annals New York Academy of Science* 1021 (2004): 296–309; E. F. Wagner, "Developmentally Informed Research on the Effectiveness of Clinical Trials: A Primer for Assessing How Developmental Issues May Influence Treatment Responses among Adolescents with Alcohol Use Problems," *Pediatrics* 121, no. S4 (2008): 337–47.

18. D. W. Zeigler, C. C. Wang, R. A. Yoast, B. D. Dickinson, M. A. McCaffree, C. B. Robinowitz, and M. L. Sterling, "The Neurocognitive Effects of Alcohol on Adolescents and College Students," *Preventive Medicine* 40 (2005): 23–32.

19. Lopez et al., "Adolescent Neurological Development"; Luna and Sweeney, "Emergence of Collaborative Brain Function."

20. Lopez et al., "Adolescent Neurological Development"; Zeigler et al., "Neurocognitive Effects."

21. J. S. Kendall and R. J. Marzano, *Content Knowledge: A Compendium of Standards and Benchmarks for K–12 Education,* 4th ed. (Denver, CO: Mid-continent Research for Education and Learning [McREL], 2008).

Chapter 3: Bringing Project Northland to Your Community

1. K. A. Komro, C. L. Perry, S. Veblen-Mortenson, K. Farbakhsh, T. L. Toomey, M. H. Stigler, R. Jones-Webb, K. Kugler, K. E. Pasch, and C. L. Williams, "Outcomes from a Randomized Controlled Trial of a Multi-component Alcohol Use Preventive Intervention for Urban Youth: Project Northland Chicago," *Addiction* 103 (2008): 606–18.

2. R. W. Edwards, P. Jumper-Thurman, B. A. Plested, E. R. Oetting, and L. Swanson, "Community Readiness: Research to Practice," *Journal of Community Psychology* 28, no. 3 (2000): 291–307.

Chapter 7: Family Involvement

1. Leadership to Keep Children Alcohol Free, *How Does Alcohol Affect the World of a Child?* NIH Publication No. 99-4670 (Bethesda, MD: National Institutes of Health, 2003).

2. D. Neumark-Sztainer, M. E. Eisenberg, J. A. Fulkerson, M. Story, and N. I. Larson, "Family Meals and Disordered Eating in Adolescents: Longitudinal Findings from Project EAT," *Archives of Pediatrics and Adolescent Medicine* 162 (2008): 17–22.

Duplicating this page is illegal. Do not copy this material without written permission from the publisher.

Chapter 8: Community Mobilization

1. Chuck McKetney and Julie Freestone, *Maintaining Effective Community Coalitions* (Martinez, CA: Contra Costa Health Services, 2005). Online at http://www.cchealth.org/groups/health_services/pdf/maintaining_effective_community_coalitions.pdf.

2. Substance Abuse and Mental Health Services Administration, *Effective Community Mobilization: Lessons from Experience,* Publication No. (SMA) 97-3131 (Rockville, MD: U.S. Department of Health and Human Services Center for Substance Abuse Prevention, 1997).

3. Substance Abuse and Mental Health Services Administration, Communities That Care® Community Planning System (Rockville, MD: U.S. Department of Health and Human Services Center for Substance Abuse Prevention, 2008). Online at https://preventionplatform.samhsa.gov.

4. Substance Abuse and Mental Health Services Administration, SAMHSA's *Prevention Platform* (Rockville, MD: U.S. Department of Health and Human Services Center for Substance Abuse Prevention, 2008). Online at https://preventionplatform.samhsa.gov/Macro/Csap/dss_portal /templates_redesign/more_about.cfm?sect_id=1&CFID=1330285&CFTOKEN=44430697&topic _id=99.

5. Helping America's Youth, *Community Guide to Helping America's Youth* (Washington, DC: The White House and the U.S. Department of Justice Office of Juvenile Justice and Delinquency Prevention).

6. R. J. Bonnie and M. E. O'Connell, Reducing and Preventing Underage Drinking: A Collective Responsibility (Washington, DC: National Academies of Science, 2004), 196.

7. Ibid.

8. K. Fleming, E. Thorson, and C. Atkin, "Alcohol Advertising Exposure and Perceptions: Links with Alcohol Expectancies and Intentions to Drink or Drinking in Underaged Youth and Young Adults," *Journal of Health Communication* 9 (2004): 3–29.

9. J. W. Grube and L. Wallack, "Television Beer Advertising and Drinking Knowledge, Beliefs, and Intentions among Schoolchildren," *American Journal of Public Health* 94 (1994): 254–59; L. B. Snyder, F. F. Milici, M. Slater, H. Sun, and Y. Strizhakova, "Effects of Alcohol Advertising Exposure on Drinking among Youth," *Archives of Pediatrics and Adolescent Medicine* 160 (2006): 18–24; A. W. Stacy, J. B. Zogg, J. B. Unger, and C. W. Dent, "Exposure to Televised Alcohol Ads and Subsequent Adolescent Alcohol Use," *American Journal of Health Behavior* 28, no. 6 (2004): 498–509.

10. Snyder et al., "Effects of Alcohol Advertising Exposure."

11. A. McClure, S. Dal Cin, J. Gibson, J. D. Sargent, "Ownership of Alcohol-Branded Merchandise and Initiation of Teen Drinking," *American Journal of Preventive Medicine* 30 (2006): 277–83.

12. K. E. Pasch, K. A. Komro, C. L. Perry, M. O. Hearst, and K. Farbakhsh, "Outdoor Alcohol Advertising Near Schools: What Does It Advertise and How Is It Related to Intentions and Use of Alcohol among Young Adolescents?" *Journal of Studies on Alcohol* 68 (2007): 587–96.

13. National Highway Traffic Safety Administration, *Traffic Safety Facts, 2005 Data: Young Drivers,* DOT HS 810 630, http://www-nrd.nhtsa.dot.gov/Pubs/810630.pdf.

14. P. M. O'Malley and A. C. Wagenaar, "Effects of Minimum Drinking Age Laws on Alcohol Use, Related Behaviors and Traffic Crash Involvement among American Youth," *Journal of Studies on Alcohol* 52, no. 5 (1991): 478–91.

Duplicating this page is illegal. Do not copy this material without written permission from the publisher.

15. J. Birckmayer and D. Hemenway, "Minimum-Age Drinking Laws and Youth Suicide, 1970–1990," *American Journal of Public Health* 89, no. 9 (1999): 1365–68.

16. A. C. Wagenaar and T. L. Toomey, "Effects of Minimum Drinking Age Laws: Review and Analyses of the Literature from 1960 to 2000," *Journal of Studies on Alcohol,* supp. 14 (2002): 206–25.

17. A. Wagenaar and M. Wolfson, "Enforcement of the Legal Minimum Drinking Age in the United States," *Journal of Public Health Policy* 15, no. 1 (1994): 37–53.

18. R. Everitt and P. Jones, "Changing the Minimum Legal Drinking Age: Its Effect on a Central City Emergency Department," *New Zealand Medical Journal* 25 (2002): 9–11.

Chapter 10: Program Evaluation

1. C. L. Perry, C. L. Williams, S. Veblen-Mortenson, T. Toomey, K. Komro, P. S. Anstine, P. McGovern, J. R. Finnegan, J. L. Forster, A. C. Wagenaar, and M. Wolfson, "Outcomes of a Community-wide Alcohol Use Prevention Program during Early Adolescence: Project Northland," *American Journal of Public Health* 86, no. 7 (1996): 956–65.

Duplicating this page is illegal. Do not copy this material without written permission from the publisher.

Cheryl L. Perry, Ph.D.

The Rockwell Distinguished Chair in Society and Health

Dr. Cheryl Perry is Professor and Regional Dean at the University of Texas, School of Public Health, Austin Regional Campus. She is also a member of the Executive Committee of the Michael & Susan Dell Center for Advancement of Healthy Living and was named the Rockwell Distinguished Chair in Society and Health in 2007. Dr. Perry joined the University of Texas School of Public Health in September 2006, after having been on the faculty at the University of Minnesota for twenty-six years.

Dr. Perry's research interests involve the design, development, implementation, and evaluation of school and community programs for young people, particularly in the areas of tobacco and alcohol use, eating, and physical activity. She served as a Principal Investigator in both the middle school and high school phases of Project Northland, and as a Co-Principal Investigator in the Chicago study. Her current projects include tobacco use prevention and cessation research in the slums in New Delhi, examining the effects of Minnesota state and local programs on youth tobacco use, and acting as a Co-Investigator on the Dell CATCH project ongoing in ninety-seven schools in Travis County, Texas. She has also just assumed the work of Senior Scientific Editor for the 2010 Surgeon General's Report on youth and tobacco use. Dr. Perry has more than 250 publications in peer-reviewed scientific literature.

Dr. Perry is a member of the Scientific Advisory Board for Communities That Care, University of Washington. In 2006, she received the Prevention Science Award from the Society for Prevention Research, and in 2005, she was recognized as one of the 100 Most-Cited Researchers in Tobacco-Related Research from the journal *Tobacco Control*.

Dr. Perry received her B.A. in Mathematics from the University of California, Los Angeles, her M.A. in Education from the University of California, Davis, and her Ph.D. in Education from Stanford University.

Carolyn L. Williams, Ph.D.

Dr. Carolyn Williams is an emeritus professor in the Division of Epidemiology in the School of Public Health at the University of Minnesota. She has more than twenty years of experience in research on Project Northland, one of the few prevention programs in U.S. schools with scientific evidence that it reduces alcohol, tobacco, and other drug use by adolescents. Project Northland provides comprehensive programs that involve adolescents, their parents, schools, and local communities. Dr. Williams's work with Project Northland included international collaborations with prevention experts in Russia and Poland, who adapted the interventions for their settings.

Dr. Williams trained in clinical psychology and has a comajor in child and family development from the University of Georgia. She has firsthand clinical experience in assessing and treating the problems she now works to prevent. She is a Fellow of the American Psychological

Duplicating this page is illegal. Do not copy this material without written permission from the publisher.

Association and a Charter Member and Diplomate of the American Board of Assessment Psychology. Dr. Williams has numerous publications in the scientific literature, including ten books. She is a coauthor of the Minnesota Multiphasic Personality Inventory for Adolescents (MMPI-A) and its alcohol-drug problem and content scales. She has taught courses on adolescent development, psychological assessment, mental health promotion, and cultural diversity and health.

Sara Veblen-Mortenson, M.S.W., M.P.H.

Ms. Veblen-Mortenson has been with the Division of Epidemiology & Community Health, School of Public Health, at the University of Minnesota since 1990. She received both her master's of Public Health and master's of Social Work degrees at the University. She served as the Project Director for Project Northland's middle school and high school study phases and for the Chicago study. Ms.Veblen-Mortenson has been responsible for the design, development, and implementation of school, family, and community-wide prevention strategies for adolescent health promotion research that focuses on substance use prevention (alcohol and other drugs) and violence prevention, and obesity prevention (physical activity and healthy eating). She has consulted with local and national organizations on alcohol prevention for middle school students. She has published many articles and book chapters on adolescent prevention programs and has presented at local and national conferences.

. . .

Duplicating this page is illegal. Do not copy this material without written permission from the publisher.

The *Program Guide* DVD includes two videos:

Project Northland Overview 16:54

This video is a general introduction to Project Northland.

Project Northland in Action 17:36

This video is intended for staff members who help deliver the curricula to students.